REVOLUTION IN THE BODY-MIND

I: Forewarning Cancer Dreams
and
The Bioplasma Concept

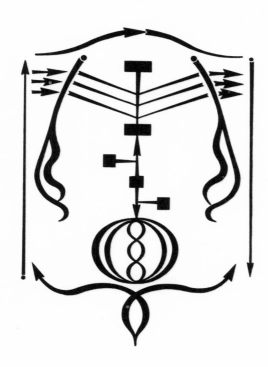

BOOKS

REVOLUTION
IN
THE BODY-MIND

by
Daniel E. Schneider, M.D.*

*Diplomate; American Board of Psychiatry and Neurology;
Life-Member, American Psychiatric Association;
Fellow, American Academy of Psychoanalysis;
Director, Foundation for Perception and Talent

THE ALEXA PRESS, INC.
EASTHAMPTON, N.Y.

Printed and Published by
THE ALEXA PRESS, INC.

Printed in the United States of America

Library of Congress Cataloging in Publication Data

Schneider, Daniel Edward, 1907-
Revolution in the body-mind.

1. Medicine, Psychosomatic—Philosophy. 2. Mind and
body. 3. Diseases—Causes and theories of causation.
4. Neuropsychiatry—Philosophy. I. Title. [DNLM: 1. Psycho-
physiologic disorders. WM90 S358r)
RC49.S348   616.08'01   77-24962
ISBN 0-930168-01-1 (v. 1)

TO THE MEMORY
OF
MY BELOVED PARENTS

ALEXANDER SCHNEIDER
*(born, Bratislava, Czechoslovakia, 1883—
died, Cleveland, Ohio, U.S.A. 1975)*

REBECCA MARKS SCHNEIDER
*(born, Lomza, Poland, 1889—
died, Cleveland, Ohio, U.S.A., 1936)*

The motif on the jacket and the book cover is an abstract design symbolizing the bioplasma-paraconscious dynamic, and the blood-pigment heart-artery circulatory system as a "coding, traveling transducer," as discussed in the text. The joined curving loop at the bottom of the design symbolizes the fused mirror-image symmetry of the body-mind.

Cf. diagram page 10.

Table of Contents

". . . Men are strong as long as they follow a strong idea. They become powerless when they desert it . . ."

—Sigmund Freud: *History of the Psychoanalytic Movement*

'Insight such as this falls to one's lot but once in a lifetime.

—Sigmund Freud: One line frontispiece to *The Interpretation of Dreams*

"One can see from the way he formulated his views that Newton felt by no means comfortable about the concept of absolute space which embodied that of absolute rest; for he was alive to the fact that nothing in experience seemed to correspond to this latter concept . . . It was the General Theory of Relativity which showed in a convincing manner the incorrectness of this view. For this theory revealed that it was possible for us, using basic principles far removed from those of Newton, to do justice to the entire range of the data of experience in a manner even more complete and satisfactory than was possible with Newton's principles.

". . . in my opinion there is *the* correct path and, moreover, it is in our power to find it. Our experience up to date justifies us in feeling sure that in Nature is actualized the ideal of mathematic simplicity. It is my conviction that pure mathematical construction enables us to discover the concepts and the laws connecting them which give us the key to the understanding of the phenomena of Nature . . ."

—Albert Einstein: "On the Method of Theoretical Physics," delivered at Oxford, England, 10 June 1933.

"Eppur il muove." (*Nevertheless it moves.*)
—Galileo Galilei: *What he was reported to have said under his breath when he bowed to the Pope in Rome condemning him to seven years of silence for daring to say that the earth moved around the sun.*

1

INTRODUCTION

The Bioplasma Concept and its Body-Mind Communication Systems. —Forewarning Cancer Dreams and Heart Attack Dreams

(Read in London, England on November 16, 1976 before the British Society for Psychosomatic Research at the Royal College of Physicians.)

In order to provide the reader with an over-all view of the large and critical task of changing our concepts of "life-process substance" away from that of the many different "plasms" now in vogue in each cell such as "nucleoplasm," "endoplasm," "cytoplasm," etc., this introduction is, in its totality, a paper on the *modern bioplasma concept* which belongs to modern "plasma physics" rather than to the early days of what was seen in the first microscopes.

The issue is not only the urgent matter of cancer, heart attack, the crippling arthritides, psychosis; it is the issue of a much greater life-span for all mankind and a much broader concept of the powers of each man's mind, with all the cogent changes for society and history that such an advance might bring.

In this first volume, it is my intention to go directly to the peculiar dreams which I have called the "forewarning dreams" of both the cancer and the heart-attack victim, doomed or rescued.

It will furthermore be the burden of this task to show how these dreams indicate the presence of a life-process substance in every cell which I have called the *bioplasma*—and how this milieu and its characteristics compel the re-evaluation of the very structure of the mind as Freud conceived it—building upon his work, as I am sure he would have wished. It will shortly be seen that just as we must conceive of a *"sending" bioplasma*—a true bioplasma in the sense of analogy to modern plasma physics—so too we must conceive of a body-to-brain and brain-mind "receiver" and monitor which acts like a "computer-composer" of all internal body-tissue information. This receiving, monitoring, computer-composer part of the human mind I have long ago named the *paraconscious* system—which has certain versatilities. It exists along-side of the classical systems of consciousness but it has *the role of organizing them* during waking and—I believe—during sleep it acts as the net "print-out" of repressed and unconscious impulses—that "print-out" we call *the dream*. The paraconscious can

2

thus be said to act as monitor-mobilizer of energies during waking and as the "dream-canvas" or "dream-screen" during sleep. It is the direct development, in my hands, of Freud's concept of a life-process "protective barrier" described by him in *Beyond the Pleasure Principle*[1] in 1920 in his concern with the victims of *shock*.

Finally, together with the concept of a bioplasma-paraconscious communication-control system—whereby brain-heart dynamics control the growth of every one of the 5000 billion cells that make up a human being—the facts of the bioplasma-paraconscious apparatus demand the re-definition of life-process as really *life-process growth* which has three major attributes namely *pulse, sentience, and genderization*. In the dreams to be presented we shall see symbolizations of these forces in ways that are expressive of the threat to life-process itself.

After the brief description of these curious dreams, I shall present a simplifying diagram illustrating the main features of the bioplasma-paraconscious systems as I conceive them. This concept has led to a new mathematics of body, brain, heart, and gender growth. The same mathematic approach bids fair to solve the residual mysteries of mitosis itself—a solution which, if true, is of critical importance to cancer control.

1. Dream Interpreted as Forewarning of Fatal Cancer in a Woman of Thirty

The dream occurs in a woman of thirty about 15 years ago before the data on cigarette smoking and lung cancer were as compelling as they are now. She was unmarried but had sexual affairs. Her entire life she had been brought up to be her "father's son." Her initials themselves spelled out the word *boy*. She ran her father's business, smoked a cigarette holding it like a man, drove a car with the same gestures and movements that a man uses—and yet she was very feminine, had no overt or any other homosexual leanings. She finally recognized that a man she loved would never marry her and her cigarette-smoking escalated to about ninety cigarettes a day.

As the frustration of the situation increased she began to manifest anxiety for the first time.

One day she reported this dream:

In the dream I am walking down the exact middle of a shopping mall with stores and store-windows on both sides.

The left side of the stores and store-windows are light and the time is day. The right side of the stores and store-windows are dark and the time is—simultaneously—night on the right side of the scene.

As I continue walking down the precise middle of the mall, I am aware that my image is being simultaneously reflected in the store windows of both sides of the scene.

But on the left side of the mall and in its store-windows my image is that of a man—though I am I. There I am dressed in my riding clothes, cap, jacket, trousers, boots, spurs and all. In my hand is a riding-crop.

On the right side of the mall and in its store-windows my image is that of a woman—as I really am—except that I am dressed in a beautiful white clinging and seductive evening gown.

As I confront the gowned image on the right side—the night-time side—suddenly the entire front of the gown is filled with red blood dripping down onto the walk.

I wake up in great anxiety.

At that time I had already begun to study the relationship of stress and drugs—like nicotine—upon psychic life. I had never before seen, in more than thirty years of experience at that time—and even now fifteen years later—a dream which so clearly contained symbols of a threatening disintegration of life-process. I knew the oncoming cigarette danger and had myself stopped all smoking.

I told her of my fears for her health and suggested she stop smoking. She refused—with complete disbelief in all the onrushing statistics—and shortly thereafter left off analytic work. But she agreed, on leaving, that if there were any symptoms (she had had a "smoker's cough" for a number of years) of any alarming kind she would submit to physical check-up.

Six months later, the internist to whom I had referred her earlier in my attempts to persuade her to the danger, phoned me to tell me that she had come because of severe pain in the back. He was convinced that there was metastasis to the spine from lung cancer. X-Ray confirmed the diagnosis. It was by now inoperable. Up to the moment of her death, she smoked the same ninety cigarettes a day.

What were the unusual features—indeed so unusual that they had no small influence in leading me finally to the concept of the bioplasma? (The concept of the paraconscious had been formed in my mind in my continuing studies of heart attack and of the subtle imagery of the heart.)

First, the precise division of the scene down a midline.

Second, the division of the scene into *two simultaneous opposite times and lightings*—nighttime on the right—day on the left.

Third, the mirror-image symmetry of the setting was violated by two opposite simultaneous modes of *sentience of Self* ranging from opposition-contrast in gender to sharp contrast in dress.

Fourth, a very violent image of the heart—the usual interpretation of the profuse bleeding would be that of castration—but my studies in the imagery of the heart had already taught me that *blood and bleeding* could have a quite different significance. It could mean the inability of the circulation to *contain* and preserve the flow of life-process substance.

Fifth, the contrast in dress and image, the blood and the impossible time and light parameters all pointed to *a violent tearing apart of gender equipment* as well as of sexual impulse direction.

A search among reported dreams over an extensive survey of the literature showed that there were many dreams having one or two of these features but none having the total constellation here described. I am however convinced that such dreams have been dreamt and reported without much if any awareness of the meaning of such distortion and division of life-process integration—involving the pulsing vital blood, the sentience of Self, the gender tearing-apart, and the time-light unreality of its simultaneous splitting modes. I am convinced—both by studies in the mathematics of the symmetry of growth and by other dreams in cases recovering from cancer—the rescued—that such forewarnings exist in persons who are in danger of being seized by the malignant neoplastic catastrophe.

Let us examine a dream in a young man who apparently has made a complete recovery after cryosurgery for a prostatic sarcoma. Three of his dreams are reported—each indicating his inner struggle to re-integrate himself. The last dream indicates that he is succeeding.

The entire series of dreams (and there have been abundant variations on the theme so clearly etched in the dream already cited) indeed suggests not necessarily an inborn disposition to the "cancer symbolizations" but definitely implies that there is—in persons likely to be afflicted—a tendency to violent gender "tearing apart" phenomena both at the physical and psychic level.

2. Dreams in a Young Man After Successful Cryosurgery for Prostatic Neoplasm

a. *I dream that I am looking at myself in a mirror. My reflected face is divided in two down the exact center. The left side is that of an old man with gray straggly hair and wrinkled aged skin. The right side is that of a beautiful young girl with smooth skin and brown hair.*

As I look at this image of myself, the reflected face of me turns to the right and gradually vanishes from my view. I wake up.

b. *I dream that I enter a square room which is divided precisely in half later in the dream. But first I see two girls stretched out on cots, their heads touching as if it were one girl reflected in a mirror. But they appear to be two girls. There is a rope around their necks. They are strangled and they are both dead.*

Then the room divides in half. The dead girls are in the right side. Now there are two similar cots or beds arranged along the left wall—except that the one nearest me is perpendicular to the one along the left wall—like the analyst chair facing toward the center of the room and toward the cots where the dead girls are stretched out.

Then I am aware that the girls are not really dead but have only been pretending. I wake up.

c. *I am lying next to a young girl who is the daughter of a friend of my father's. I insert my fingers into her vagina.*

Then the scene changes. I am now in a room with the father of the girl—or a man like him with whom I am friendly. In the center of the room is a large box. And in the center of the box is a clear empty flask.

As I reach to touch the empty flask, it is suddenly enveloped in a blue electric sparking and dangerous halo.

I withdraw my hand and I vow to renounce the flask forever.

The first two dreams clearly indicate the influence of the analysis—but with sharp unconscious resistance. In the first dream though he makes his "opposite gender face" turn away—he retains the aging and aged face, an image related to awareness of the cost of the ablation of the prostate. In the first dream the simultaneous times and the midline division are sharply present. . . . In the second dream, his violent "death by strangulation" of the dead girl—seen as *two* in the mirror-structure of the scene—is rescinded by the setting of the analyst and himself on the later left division of the room. . . . In the third dream, corresponding to an emergence of new capacities, he still is reaching *to steal* (hence his fingers) the gender equipment of a girl. Then he tries to take its "creative essence"—the uterine flask in the box—but vows to relinquish his yearnings to possess the gender opposite to his own.

In all these dreams—the dream in the fatal lung cancer case the the dream in the rescued young man—one can hardly avoid noting that the violence of the gender "tearing apart" is almost that of the so-called trans-sexual. It will be interesting to see what the total life-span of the trans-sexual will encounter in the way of malignancy—should any trans-sexual record his whole life history.

Before describing the heart attack dreams—again those of fatal outcome, and the apparently rescued at least for a while—we shall present a diagram of the bioplasma-paraconscious mechanism. It is of course highly schematic and condenses many years of study both in the mathematics of life-process growth and in the architecture of brain-mind transformations which requires the presence of the paracon-scious as well as the "sending" bioplasma using the "travelling transducer" of blood-circulatory vessel sonic-acoustic characteristics.*

But, as we approach our diagram, two additional cancer dreams are briefly described for the sake of, hopefully, sketching the full range of the phenomena.

3. Dream of Being Transected in a Case of Lung Cancer

A sixty year old man who has been a heavy cigarette smoker and has developed the usual dry hacking "smoker's cough" begins to have a strange dream that repeats itself almost identically again and again. At first he discounts it even though his brother died almost twenty years before of lung cancer also following very heavy smoking and indulgence in various drugs.

Finally, he tells me the repetitive dream:

I dream that I am in the army again, this time in combat areas though in reality I never got into combat. I am dressed in the uniform I wore so long and I am now in a wide open space and search frantically for cover.

At last I see a single large tree and, as I make for it, I am delighted to find that it has a hollowed-out trunk into which I climb and am therefore completely merged with the body of the tree.

Then I hear machine-gun fire. . . . But at the same moment that I hear the sound of the gun going rat-a-tat-tat, *I look down and see that the bullets are reaching the tree and are cutting me in half methodically going from the left side of my lower chest to the right, clear across my body.*

*Cf. The clear proof of the presence of ultrasonic frequencies (29,000 cps) capable of being transmitted by the bloodstream to auditory brain centers. (Bellucci and Schneider[8])

I wake from the dream in great anxiety.

He is persuaded to go for a check-up. A small neoplasm on the left lower lobe of the lung, fortunately still circumscribed and without any evidence of metastasis, is discovered.

He is operated at once. It is now six years since the surgery and he remains well.

Here the forewarning dream is heeded in time. Remarkable again is the specific inclusion of the direction *from left to right*. (He is right-handed.) But also noteworthy is the *transection of the body* at precisely the level of the neoplasm, undoubtedly connected with pleural sensations he was beginning to admit to consciousness.

And while the first lung cancer dream cited above is concerned with the mirror-image gender division of the *Self*, this dream is a different kind of mutilation of Self. It contains the symbolic "running for cover" into the "womb-torso" of the tree-trunk—and yet this is only—in the dream—an illusory safety. Nothing can escape the danger, and the doom of combat.

The uniform of a long ago war and of a long ago danger (which at that time had never materialized) is now in the dream a real and present danger.

Moreover, *there is no way the transection of the body by machine-gun fire can be interpreted as a "wish"*—unless, in order to see the coherence of original Freudian theory, the "wish" here is the "death-wish"—precisely the phenomenon Freud discussed in his brilliant *Beyond the Pleasure Principle* where he notes first the obsessive-compulsive repetition dream and symptom formation of cases of shock, and secondly therefore postulates the presence of and the *rupture of a life-process protective barrier*—that barrier or monitor which I have developed into the paraconscious system to be portrayed here in the diagram below.

A fourth and final cancer dream completes the adumbration of the impact of the body-cell malignant change "sent" to the "receiving" life-process protective paraconscious—now utterly overwhelmed.

4. Dream of the Explosion of the Body in Terminal Rapidly Metastasizing Cancer

This dream is reported by the patient's nurse, the only one to whom he had confided any apprehension.

The patient was a successful attorney in his late sixties. He is taken to the hospital for surgery in an acute gall-bladder attack.

At the operation the surgeons discover they are confronted by a malignant neoplasm of the gall-bladder and that it has already metastasized extensively leaving its victim only about two months to live.

The surgeons are compelled to tell him the truth—which he utterly disbelieves or at least represses his ability to trust the report. For 10 days he continues in this state of denial and a remarkable equanimity.

Then one night he awakens from a dream with great anxiety. His report to the nurse was brief:

I dreamt that my entire body exploded, shattering into a thousand fragments. My terror was indescribable."

There is little doubt that these are dreams in which the body-cells in their now disorganized and malignant growth are violently "tearing apart" the once coherent and fortified sense of organization of the Self. These four cases illustrate all too eloquently the presence of a body-mind communication system generally operating subliminally but now reporting all the degrees of disruption to a once effective and supreme "center control"—which records to the end.

That these dreams are utterly different in design from forewarning heart attack dreams we shall see following the brief presentation of the diagram of the bioplasma concept and its body-mind communication system.

In the diagram it will be seen that three major changes— *revolutionary when compared to our conventional confusion*—are made in basic neural, cellular and circulatory physiology. The facts— not any primary wish to "make a theory"—compel these changes.

As one scrutinizes the diagram one will note that:

(1) The paraconscious system (development of the Freudian life-protecting barrier) is placed in such a way as to monitor and to mobilize and to shape the flow of mental energies with reference to the inner world of the body as well as the outer world. It must be conceived to have a vortical or rotatory motion—in relation to the normal cerebral dominance from left to right—and yet to "rotate" during waking in relation to *first*, incoming usual perception and outgoing usual action, and *second*, to incoming information from the "sending system" of the bioplasma body-cell, and *third*, in relation to the hypothalamic-pituitary out-going flow back to the body-cells. . . . At night the "rotating blades" of the paraconscious swing upward and thus play a role in inducing sleep by dampening down the flow of perceptual-actional forces. We conceive that as this paraconscious activity takes place, its "underneath surfaces" become the *dream-screen*. . . . Further it will be seen that the paraconscious stands in

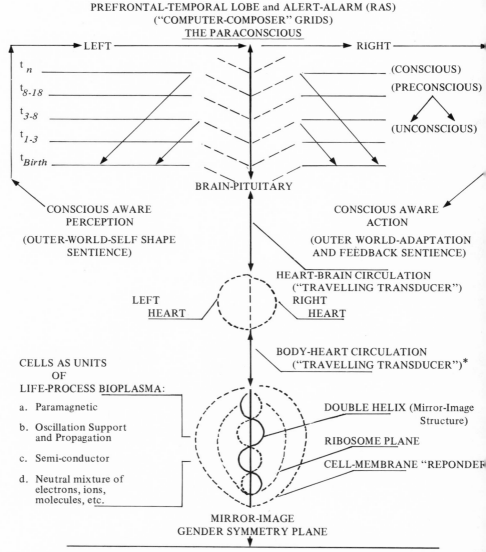

PREFRONTAL-TEMPORAL LOBE and ALERT-ALARM (RAS)
("COMPUTER-COMPOSER" GRIDS)
THE PARACONSCIOUS

LEFT ──────────► ◄────────── RIGHT

t_n _____   (CONSCIOUS)

t_{8-18} _____   (PRECONSCIOUS)

t_{3-8} _____

t_{1-3} _____   (UNCONSCIOUS)

t_{Birth} _____

BRAIN-PITUITARY

CONSCIOUS AWARE   CONSCIOUS AWARE
PERCEPTION   ACTION

(OUTER-WORLD-SELF SHAPE   (OUTER WORLD-ADAPTATION
SENTIENCE)   AND FEEDBACK SENTIENCE)

HEART-BRAIN CIRCULATION
("TRAVELLING TRANSDUCER")
LEFT   RIGHT
HEART   HEART

BODY-HEART CIRCULATION
CELLS AS UNITS   ("TRAVELLING TRANSDUCER")*
OF
LIFE-PROCESS BIOPLASMA:

a. Paramagnetic   DOUBLE HELIX (Mirror-Image
                                              Structure)
b. Oscillation Support
   and Propagation   RIBOSOME PLANE

c. Semi-conductor   CELL-MEMBRANE "REPONDER

d. Neutral mixture of
   electrons, ions,
   molecules, etc.

MIRROR-IMAGE
GENDER SYMMETRY PLANE

**DIAGRAM: THE CONCEPT OF THE BIOPLASMA-PARACONSCIOUS
BODY-MIND COMMUNICATION-CONTROL SYSTEMS**

*Evidence for the blood and pigment system as a "traveling transducer" now comes dramatically (*Medical World News*, May 2, 1977, pg. 23) in the "startling" fact that hemodialysis by a "kidney machine" in certain schizophrenics cleared up psychotic symptoms, reported by J. R. Cade of the University of Florida joined by Dr. Herbert Wagemaker of the University of Louisville. They suspect a "toxic substance accumulation" due to inherited enzymatic detect.

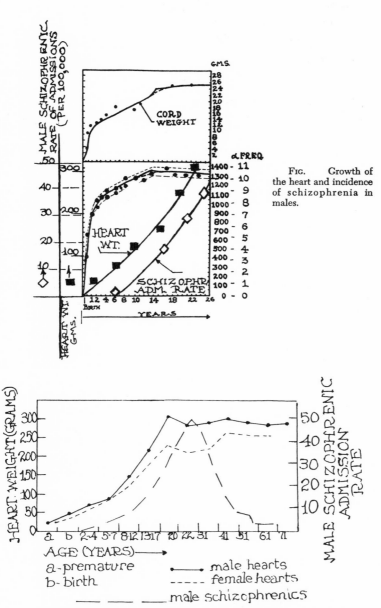

Fig.   Growth of the heart and incidence of schizophrenia in males.

Fig.   Correlation between growth of the heart and schizophrenia in males.

such a position as to co-exist with all the systems of consciousness we know—but at the same time to be quite different from conscious, pre-conscious, and unconscious process—though accessible to and in communication with all of them. . . . In addition, in the diagram, the paraconscious "axis" is placed at the plane of mirror-image symmetry (it might be called the "psychic corpus callosum" and thus connects the limbic brain to the prefrontal lobes and the temporal lobe of the neocortex.) . . . Through its connection with the reticular activating system and the sonic-characteristics of the temporal lobe, it acts as the "receiver" of information from the circulating blood and other sonic-acoustic forces in a manner now to be described as it is illustrated in the diagram.*

(2) It will be noted that the circulatory system is here given the sobriquet of a "travelling transducer." Some data indicate that the red blood cell pigment may do its respiratory work by specific forms of "electron transfer" as the acoustic force of the heart propels the blood at a rate specific for every species of the higher forms of life. We may finally arrive at a rational concept as to why red blood cells are made and destroyed every day. Indeed their task is both incessant and enormous.

But, from the biophysical point of view, the combination of a circulatory pressure, an acoustic pulse, and electron-transfer at the tissue-cell membranes all over the body does indicate the presence of a circulating piezo-electric system, extremely subtle and probably making its oxygen-carbon dioxide interchanges at the membrane subject to transducer laws. . . . As it receives its carbon-dioxide and other metabolic wastes from every tissue cell, so too, it is my concept, that it is given the means to "report" to the brain—by the very same process—any deviation from the usual "oscillations" and "oscillation frequency" of the fundamental organizing apparatus of the tissue cells, i.e. from cell-membrane, ribosome and double helix of the 5000 billion cells that make a human body.**

The moment that we admit this possibility into our conceptions the cancer dreams we have reported—and the heart attack dreams we shall briefly describe—take on new coloration as indeed forewarning "net print-outs" trying to tell us something more than our sexual frustrations are being "sent" by whatever code from each tissue. (Indeed the "code" may be *infolded* in the biochemical-to-biophysical

---

*The presence of an ultrasonic system was first described in my *The Growth Concept of Nervous Integration* (1949 monograph)[9]
**These "oscillations" are part and parcel of the process of the motional forces between electron donors and electron acceptors resulting in appropriate "coded" transformations into biochemical substances in tissue and blood.

transformations within the "travelling transducer" of the circulatory system.) . . . *These forewarning dreams tell us that the very architecture of our being is being undermined, distorted, and alienated from the once normal coherence and defense of what we may call the "bioplasma community" of the tissue-systems of our bodies.*

Not only cancer and heart attack but also schizophrenia may come under the same aegis.

In 1968[2] I presented evidence that the heart appeared indeed to act as though it were an extra-cerebral hallucinogenic pump creating the syndromes of insanity. What led me to this idea, then, was the fact that the age-incidence of schizophrenia "followed" *not the growth of the brain but the growth of the heart.* I reproduce the relevant figure from that paper here and now to indicate another piece of evidence that the circulatory system may indeed—by virtue of its complex pigment chemistry—induce a change *not by creating an actual hallucinogen* (though that is possible) but rather by an alteration in the transducer effects from body to brain having such a net effect in the brain itself.

All these considerations and many others (including a new and rational mathematics of growth[3]) thus led to the bioplasma concept next to be considered as shown in the diagram.

(3) The term "bioplasma" has nothing in common with the old term "cytoplasm" and blood "plasma."

Rather the term is employed on the basis of an *analogy* to modern plasma used in very high temperature plasma physics, in thermonuclear research. No body-cell could sustain such temperatures. Hence we must conceive of a *bio*-plasma in which temperature-mechanisms have developed over the millions of years of evolution compatible with life-process and *life-process growth* as we know it. (We will not indulge in the old "philosophical" debates as to whether "intrinsic" life-process grows or not.) And, in such a bioplasma capable of embodying the design of and sustaining life-process growth—pulsing, sentient, and genderizing—the interactions between cell-membrane, double helix, and ribosome are largely *paramagnetic* related to electron paramagnetic resonance rather than to electromagnetism as it is seen in the thermonuclear laboratory.*

But otherwise the bioplasma has these characteristics—in our concept—which are analogous to those in modern thermonuclear plasma:

(1) it is dominated by paramagnetic interactions;

*There is evidence now accumulating, since this was written, that each organelle within the cell, has its specific electric potentials, thus laying a basis for bioplasma paramagnetic interactions between organelles.
Cf. Giulian and Diacumakos, *New Scientist,* 17 February, 1977.

(2) it is capable of supporting and propagating oscillation frequencies specific to that plasma; (such as the EKG and EEG);

(3) it is capable of acting as a semi-conductor—as is the brain-cell and the cells in the heart's Bundle of His; and finally, as in thermonuclear plasma,

(4) it is a *neutral* mixture of electrons, ions, molecules, etc.

I cannot in so brief a report indicate the exciting manner in which it is possible to develop a new and rational concept of growth and perhaps even to solve most of the residual mysteries of mitosis on the basis of a life process growth, pulsing, sentient and genderizing in an evolution-designed true bioplasma. As I have already stated, those mathematic studies appear later in this book.

The remaining burden of this communication is to show the forewarning heart attack dreams and to conclude with another form of dream alerting us to a normal growth process in the human body—namely the pregnancy dream which sometimes seems to forecast even the sex of the foetus.

We proceed now to the forewarning heart attack dreams.

In 1953-1956 long before Friedman and Rosenman attempted to forge a valid outline of the "heart attack personality" on the basis of statistics and certain traits which appear to be entirely irrelevant and misleading, I had described what I called "coronary character" in my book *The Image of the Heart.*[4] (cf. pgs. 18-26). There I detailed the four major categories of personality traits in the "coronary man." *First,* he exhibited a peculiar controlled tension; to such men true relaxation, particularly sexual relaxation spells danger.* *Second,* however "sweet" (or superpaternal) his manner, he is always in a physical hurry; not uncommonly he affects a distinct kind of hurrying gait. And, he is constantly hurrying *away* from a deeply concealed dread—but thinks he is in an important hurry toward some outward project. *Third,* he is obsessed by ambition in a very peculiar way—in a way belonging to an intense and secret fantasy reflected in ambitions for money and fame which are thinly veiled bizarre "goals." Success—as well as failure—may thus precipitate attacks. To conceal the guilt of the fantasy he may exercise rituals of "self-purification" frequently secretly performed. *Fourth,* he has many symptoms and signs of a

---

*The recent discovery by G. B. Phillips of Columbia University (N.Y. Times, April 27, 1977) of the critical shift of the sexual hormones estradiol and testosterone in "heart attack men" throws a confirming light upon our constant insistence (1956-1967) and beyond to the present time that heart attack is sexual-hormonal in relation to rage-terror stress and defective paraconscious monitoring. Cf. Especially my *Psychoanalysis of Heart Attack*, 1967, Dial Press.

severely split identification process. In this framework one is prepared to find that almost all early "coronary attacks" are in men with severe disturbances in the orgasm itself. (I described this in detail in my *Psychoanalysis of Heart Attack*[5] in 1967.)

In many ways such men are aware of the fact that something is wrong with their arterial systems—not infrequently because of the vertiginous aftermath of their incredible rages and even more impossible exhausting drives for money—approaching almost a cannibalistic fury.

Consider this dream in a man with such character suffering from anginal attacks and other forms of arterial spasm symptomatology.

5. Dream of the Cooked Dog

I dream that I come home for dinner very, very hungry. My wife says she has a hot dog for me.

But when she serves the dog—he is no frankfurter. He is instead my own pet dog who has the same name as my brother, who in my childhood of deprivation and hunger, died in the bed in which we slept together.

Nevertheless I begin to lift my fork to stick it into his flank when he opens his big eyes and rolls them pleadingly up toward mine.

That even doesn't stop me. I stick my fork into his flank and as I do so I awaken with a sharp pain across my chest, and down my left arm.

The contrast between what we might call the "fabric and the design" of this kind of dream and the cancer dreams is quite striking. In all heart attack dreams both before the attack and between attacks the *preoccupation with animal symbols* is extremely intense. In my experience the animal symbols of dreams are not purely sexual—as Freud once thought—but rather combined heart-sexual imagery of a very different kind. In these symbols I believe it is *animal* as symbol of *animation and pulse*—of life-process itself. The bird is implicit in the many literary symbols of the "heart fluttering in the bosom."

This man with the cooked dog dream I followed for twenty years. His angina came under control in distinct proportion to his (not always successful) efforts to control both the obvious rage and the inner dread of impoverishment which to him meant the early death of a brother. When he died it was a cerebral death in his seventies, even though the presenting symptoms had for so long been "coronary."

Consider the "animal" symbols in the next two dreams in a man with a heart attack by 46 years of age followed by several heart attacks and finally a fatal stroke.

6. The Dream of the Magic Mouse and the Amputated Cat

I dream that my young daughter is dancing around the room holding a vase . . . There is something inside the vase squirting streams of water out of it . . . She shakes the vase hard and a small mouse leaps out of the lid of the vase and falls to the ground stunned.

It is a strange-looking little mouse with a group of rods or tubes sticking out from around its mouth . . . My young daughter cries out that it is in agony and that I should do something about it . . .

I stamp my foot on it until I crush the life out of it—with a horrible feeling in my stomach as I stamp it to death."

Among the many associations to this dream was that of the mouse as the one of "hickory, dickory, dock—the mouse ran up the clock." The symbol of the small animal as the "life-animation" symbol includes his fear of his daughter's rape and impregnation as well as the terror that his own "mouse-clock" will now "run down"—as in the nursery rhyme.

Then there is a second dream shortly after the first.

I called an old carpenter to come and fix a box for me.

Then he revised it, thus:

My wife and I were driving in a car; in the dream we had a cat along.

The cat leaped out of the car and her tail was cut off and bleeding.

I called the old carpenter and he came and fixed her up—sewed the tail back on the cat.

This kind of dream indicates the inner struggle of a split identification in the heart attack man. It is a dream portending death. He was dead several years later after repeated attacks.

7. The Dream of the Self as Horse

This is the dream of a man who has had three heart attacks—will undergo analysis and will stay free of attacks—until after interrupting analysis, he returns to cigarettes and induces another attack.

This is one of his dreams indicating his defiance.

I am on the way to the racetrack, which I love, to see a horse I am interested in, run.

On the way a group of stableboys in jockey clothes and boots try to stop my car.

I keep going straight ahead and they are all drawn under my car as though it were a tank. I get out and all I can find of them are some boots hanging on the rear bumper.

I am summoned before a judge and jury but in the witness-box when I am asked questions I can not reply in words. Instead steam comes out from my clothes as though I myself had run the race.

These dreams in greatly condensed form are presented for contrast with the cancer dreams. It is quite clear that a different system of cells are signalling to the "dream-maker and the dream-screen." There is no play with symmetry-disturbance of gender, no transection of the body, no explosion of self. Instead the symbolizations are of dog, mouse, cat, horse.

There is no doubt that in hundreds and thousands of dreams the two categories "borrow" symbolizations from each other in the infinite permutations of dream-formation.

But neither is there any mistaking the pure form of the forewarning dream in either case: cancer or heart attack.

One other piece of evidence of still another tissue and its signalling mode—namely the pregnancy dream which occurs *only at the true moment of impregnation.* There are many variations but all of them indicate that the impregnation changes which take place at the time of fertilization signal almost immediately to the "receiving paraconscious." Here is an example in a young married woman:

I had a dream that there was an open shoe-box. Suddenly a purring lively kitten with a pink ribbon tied around its neck jumped into the box.

Immediately the sides of the shoe-box began to fold over by themselves. They apparently developed a zipper which automatically zipped the shoe-box tight. I could feel the frightened kitten beating in and against the side of the box.

Here is the manifestation of the combined symbols of the impregnated uterus and the "beat" of the kitten (the pulsing image of the heart) indicating how the arteries as well as the heart are equipped with a signalling system belonging to the "life-process substance" of our bodies—the bioplasma—capable not only of sustaining and supporting life-process growth, pulsing, sentient, and genderizing but also capable of generating and propagating specific oscillatory codes via the "travelling transducer" of the circulatory apparatus and its subtle electron-transfering enzymes of the pigment chemistry resident in blood cells as they maintain tissue respiration. (Cf. Dickerson et al.[6] on electron-transfer via *cytochrome c* in respiration and photosynthesis.)*

Finally, the futility of trying to ascribe the disease of "plaque" changes in the coronary arteries and in the lenticulo-striate arteries to the so-called "Type A Personality" of Friedman and Rosenman[7] is evident in their book in which the last third is an exhortation to the "victim" or likely victim to change his personality—which is anyhow a secondary and not a primary phenomenon in the causation. One might just as well exhort the victim of familial xanthomatosis to change his character and so avoid the unavoidable tumors of the arteries which destroy whole families from children of 10 years of age to men of 50 years of age—sometimes a father and a daughter at the same time . . . Nowhere is the necessity to face the challenge of the nature of the bioplasma of the arterial cell itself—and *especially its genetic and genderizing components*—more heavily obvious than in the rather empty "cheer-leader" approach of the authors of the Type A Personality mythology . . . They nowhere investigate for example those dynamic personality conflicts which indicate basic gender-sexual disease as has so long been known in the predilection of the male overwhelmingly to coronary heart attack and to coronary heart disease in general. Just as they have taken no cognizance of my previous work from 1953-1967 in which coronary character was first described and its various unpredictable character types outlined, so too their statistical studies neglect the fact that the basic disease affects the arteries to the emotional centers themselves.

The fact that lenticulo-striate artery disease classically— especially in vascular hypertension—accompanies coronary disease ought long ago to have alerted us to the possibility that heart attack as we know it is *a disease of brain-heart monitors*—in brief a disease of the brain-structures which I have included under the brain-mind transforming system named the *paraconscious* functioning as "bridge" between brain and mind.

A glance at the diagram of Figure 1 (of this introductory paper) illustrating the bioplasma concept will reveal that both cancer and heart attack may be end-results of defective monitoring by the paraconscious, rendered deficient by all the pollutants and viruses indicated in cancer itself. Furthermore there is some evidence which I

*Cf Early discussion of importance of pigment systems in *The Growth Concept of Nervous Integration* (9).

can not include here which indicates that the arterial "plaque" may indeed be a form of disordered life-process growth, and repair.**

The problem of brain tumors themselves—and the curious forewarning dreams seen in these neoplasms of brain parenchyma and supportive tissue must be left for a separate report. Here I can only state that I have seen certain dreams in persons who are largely unanalyzable but who show the classical "Witzelsucht" (wittiness) of the frontal lobe brain-tumor and who may have such dreams years before the tumor finally makes itself manifest.***

Summary: Forewarning dreams heralding cancer and heart attack (as well as announcing impregnation) illustrate the theory of body-mind communication systems based upon a "sending" bioplasma from every tissue cell in the organism to the "receiving" and monitoring "computer-composer" equipment of the paraconscious.

Our studies in the mathematics of life-process growth as well as new research on electron-transfer function of cytochrome enzymes in respiration and photosynthesis make possible considering the circulatory system a "travelling transducer," transmitting information via chemical and other "codes" to the paraconscious from the bioplasma.

The bioplasma of every cell in the body, analogous to thermonuclear plasma and subject to the laws of plasma physics, is characterized by its dominant paramagnetic interactions, its action as a semi-conductor, its support and propagation of oscillations such as the EEG and EKG, and neutral admixture of ions, electrons, molecules, etc. The bioplasma concept in no way runs athwart the great science of molecular biology.

The dreams presented categorized as *forewarning* have the potentiality of saving life and enhancing longevity—if the forewarning aspects are mastered *by the analyst and heeded by the patient.*

November 16, 1976   Daniel E. Schneider, M.D.
London, England

**As this book goes to press, there appears the brilliant work of Benditt, in the February 1977 issue of the *Scientific American* journal showing that the plaque arises from mutant muscle cells becoming mobile and moving into the intima and its endothelium to create the classical "bulge" which ulcerates and is then invaded by fats. Here too Benditt illustrates that both cancer and arteriosclerosis are diseases of life-process growth as we have so long maintained.
***Cf The case of the famous American composer, George Gershwin.

REFERENCES

1. Freud, Sigmund: *Beyond the Pleasure Principle*, The International Psychoanalytic Press, London, England, 1922.
2. Schneider, Daniel E.: *Anxiety Preceding a Heart Attack—Effect of Person. (The Heart as a Potential Hallucinogenic Pump.)* Presented before the Society of Medical Analysts at the Academy of Medicine, New York, N.Y. Dec. 4, 1968. Published in *Conditional Reflex*, July-Sept. 1969, pgs. 169-186.
3. Schneider, Daniel E.: *Revolution in the Body-Mind:* The New Science of The Bioplasma and the Concept of Life Process as Life-Process Growth Pulsing, Sentient and Genderizing (In process of publication for early 1977 by the Alexa Press, Easthampton, N.Y.)
4. Schneider, Daniel E.: *The Image of the Heart*, The International Universities Press, N.Y., N.Y., 1956.
5. Schneider, Daniel E.: *Psychoanalysis of Heart Attack*, The Dial Press, N.Y., N.Y. 1967.
6. Dickerson, R.E., Timkovich, R., Almassy, R.J.: *The Cytochrome Fold and the Evolution of Bacterial Energy Metabolism*, Journal of Molecular Biology, vol. 100, No. 4, 1976, pgs. 473-491.
7. Friedman, M. and Rosenman, R.H.: *Type A Behavior and Your Heart*, A.A. Knopf, 1974.
8. Bellucci, Richard J. and Schneider, Daniel E.: *Some Observations on Ultrasonic Perception in Man*, Amr. Otol., Rhinol., and Laryngol., vol. 71, no. 3, p. 719, Sept. 1962.
9. Schneider, Daniel E.: *The Growth Concept of Nervous Integration*, Monograph No. 78 in Nervous and Mental Disease Monograph Series (1949)

FOREWORD

The Presentation of the Equations

Because of the complexity of this portion of our work, for the sake of as much clarity as can be achieved and of as much brevity as can be accomplished, I have decided upon the following plan of presentation:
  1. Brief Statement of the Three Major New Concepts
  2. The Analogies to Modern Physics Used As a Basis for the Equations
  3. A List of the Equations and Presentation of Tables and Charts

The derivations of the equations will have to be postponed for later detailed preparation. In each case the basis will be stated however. Those who find the subject of interest—*the work has been designed in the hope that the equations can be used in urgently necessary research in cancer, psychosis, heart attack and stroke*—and who are mathematically and biophysically trained will have little difficulty in discerning the complete derivation. For those who are more interested in the possible applications clinically, in the treatment of people, of the new concept of the "mind" proposed here, the derivations will not deter them from at least contemplating new horizons such as Freud himself began to see and yet could not reach.

Most important to me is that these new vistas should be steadily illuminated by those who come after me. I believe they are there—not in more "verbiage" of various "social theories of the mind" but with new implications for a much greater longevity for mankind, if we can solve the dilemmas of the body-mind. Man's brain-heart, heart-body, and body-mind are really capable of much more power than we realize—in love and work on this planet—in whatever conquests of outer space (e.g. plans to build earth-satellite colonies) our descendants undertake.

Toward that goal we have to know how every cell of the human body is present in the net "print-out" of the human mind by that system I call the "computer-composer paraconscious,"—and how dreams really are capable, like intuition itself, of warning us of inner as well as outer impending disasters.

In all this work, I have had the constant help of my good friend, Mr. R. Talbott Miller in supplying me with data essential and relevant—and with loyal encouragement, in the labors of this first volume, as well as in the volumes on clinical aspects of *Revolution In The Body-Mind* to follow.

1. Brief Statement of the Three Major New Concepts

Three major concepts underlie the equations which are the main burden of this part—all three represent not revision of concepts but revolution in certain fundamental assumptions.

Yet, to my way of thinking about the facts they are not really revolutionary at all although they do reverse perhaps an entire century of an erroneous, even superstitious, separation of life-process from living growth.

The dictum appears to have been that "life-process does not grow"—to summarize in my own words what theorists of growth have been believing for well over a hundred—perhaps thousands of—years. This has had far-reaching consequences in all aspects of medicine— even perhaps in all our philosophies—and particularly affects our current increasing urgent necessities to solve the scourges of cancer, psychosis, heart attack and stroke.

To avoid a great deal of discussion better suited to a much longer essay, let us state the three major ideas upon which this work rests.

The *first* is that life-process has three major ingredients and a fourth "inevitability." *Life-process is always pulsing, sentient, and genderizing,* in any real meaningful formulation of what it means to be alive—from amoeba to man. The fourth "inevitability" is the fact that it has—for each individual—a termination called "death." And yet, despite the Biblical allotment of "three-score and ten" years, there is no real inevitability about how great a span of life we may be able to achieve, in a state of adequate pulsing of our hearts and of sentience of our brain-mind. *The laws of longevity are a necessary consequence of our definition of life-process as life-process growth pulsing, sentient, and genderizing.*

The *second* "revolutionary" idea is that the moment of fertilization—when the "one and only" sperm penetrates the ovum—is the moment when the brain-heart design characteristic of any of the higher species is established. It is therefor a corollary of this point of view that the body—apart from brain and heart—is designed by the double helix made by fertilization to serve the necessities of the pulsing heart-arterial system and the brain-cord-nerve system. Otherwise neither pulsing nor sentience nor genderization could be maintained coherently.

This latter idea is best paraphrased simply thus: it is not true that first God made Man out of clay and then "breathed" life into him. First the elementary "cells" had to "breathe"—and carry that breath, the result of constantly developing forms of organization for pulsing and sentience to higher levels—still evolving. *Man* is still evolving.

The immediate mathematic and biophysical consequence of this change in orientation is that—in this work—we can not treat growth by any of the "time-honored" formulae (always and forever created by avoiding the challenge of life-process pulsing, sentient and genderizing growth) based on the sheer dead *numbers* of cells or *dimensions* of length and width. We can not treat growth even on the Newtonian analogy as "cells shot out of the cannon of fertilization" and undergoing in their trajectory Newtonian laws of motion, important as it is to recognize that the laws of motion may be demonstrated in the trajectories of growth. In this work we treat life-process growth on the basis of relativistic and paramagnetic characteristics which supersede Newton and yet embrace and use all the brilliance of Newton, Maxwell and Faraday.

The concept of life-process growth pulsing, sentient, and genderizing, moves us into the modern world of Einstein, Bohr, Rutherford, Planck, Born, and Heisenberg and all the other "poets of modern physics" who literally have discovered what the incomparable Shakespeare called "the music of the spheres." In essence every single individual cell of the approximately 5000 billion cells that make up the human body is as relativistic and paramagnetic in its integrated activities as is the fertilized ovum itself. In this way we refuse the old concept that the body grows and then the "brain and heart just come along" in proportion to body mass, or cell-number, length and width; instead we state that—to serve the pulsing heart and sentient brain-mind—every cell in the body is "tooled" in its relativistically-powered "vehicles" by which the DNA-RNA mechanism carries the coded instruction via messenger and transfer RNA to the cells' ribosomes— *to repeat,* every cell in the body is "tooled" to the biomagnetic nature of the electrophoretic "vehicle" by which the RNA "commutes" from nucleus to ribosome and back again to the "code-center" of the DNA double helix. At "code-center" in the nucleus as well as in the outside cytoplasm there are unanswered problems of the movement of electrons in their orbits in which the electron acts like a bar magnet to produce the well-known phenomenon of EPR or electronic paramagnetic resonance. *It is this motion which is integrated from the beginning with brain and heart pulsing.* Nor do we need to remind anyone that the "brain-wave" like the "electroencephalogram" is just such a "clockwork" of electronic and paramagnetic motion. What is new and revolutionary here is that all the evidence—accumulating from research centers all over the world—is that the brain-heart and mind-brain "control" operates to direct the transactions of every cell in the body not merely by "oxygen to the cell" nor even by "feedback" from the inner world of the cell and the outer world of whatever environment. *The brain-heart and mind-brain control over every cell in the body* in all likelihood *operates by specific centrally directed biomagnetic fields with equally specific limits both in the space and time of all organ transactions established by the necessities to keep brain sentient and heart pulsing*—"until death do us part."

From 1936-1949, culminating in my first monograph *The Growth Concept of Nervous Integration*[1] in 1949, I stated what has since been proven by the brilliant research of Guillemin[2] and Schally[3] that the brain directly communicated its influences to the pituitary via the hypothalamus. And in this manner it was possible from 1936-1949 to establish the fact that *the brain acted as a force of growth to control the potentiation-kinesis equilibrium of the entire body.* On this basis we derived the necessary equations back there to prove the point to the degree that a sheer simplified mathematic proof could be established.

What we add to our second "revolutionary" concept then is that the true meaning of a "hormone" is not merely that of a "messenger" who comes and goes with instructions in hand—but rather as a more or less *resident delegate*—for however short a stay—however re-supplied and refurbished—to ensure the coherent tooling of every cell with the necessities and demands of the "center-control" i.e. heart-brain and brain-mind. *A hormone is a resident "biomagnetic" delegate, resupplied and refurbished by the heart-arterial system in a way that will demand a totally new concept of what an artery is.* As this work develops here, we shall adumbrate and elaborate the concept of the "new artery" which is much more than a "pipeline" and, instead, plays a critical role in psychosis, cancer, heart attack and stroke—even in senile dementia and perhaps the torturing arthritides themselves. It will be important to recall—as we get to this part of the problem—that arterial damage takes place *upstream* to the organ *before* the "capillary bridge" to the tissue is reached. Here too we shall find the challenge of the "electron clockwork" in arterial cells themselves.

To summarize and to go on to the third of the "revolutionary" concepts: *first*, life-process is life-process pulsing, sentient and genderizing growth, and growth can not be separated from alive pulse and sentience in any living thing; growth is not a thing of dead cell-number and inert dimension: *second*, there is a central control of pulse, sentience and genderization from the moment of fertilization in however primordial a form; the meaning of fertilization—and its moment—is the establishment of a brain-heart design unique to that species and to any given individual; the central control by heart-brain and brain-mind transformations takes place via biomagnetic mechanisms—from hypothalamus to pituitary—which we have called "hormones" but act much more like resident delegates from the "center" to every cell in the body, where the biomagnetic operations of the DNA-RNA mechanisms in the coding, instructing, transfering and manufacturing facilities are part of a much larger issue to which, for brevity, we might assign the sobriquet "electron clockwork"—and soon we shall describe it for the purposes of our equations by its proper name: "electron paramagnetic resonance"; and, as a corollary, a new concept of an artery is demanded by this orientation and indeed by the facts themselves as they present themselves in cancer, psychosis, senile dementia, heart attack and stroke, and even the arthritides where arterial supply indeed acts like it has parted company from the articulations of the bony-cartilaginous system.

The *third* concept has to do with what is called "the mind" whose influence on life-process pulsing, sentient and genderizing growth, is enormous. Indeed it is entirely dubious—from the present point of view—if the term is at all correct. What we must really mean, certainly in modern times, by "mind," is that there are a series of brain-transformations lending a rhythmic structure—dependent upon sleep, rest, fatigue, and awakening—of all our learned experiences taking in the new and repressing the pain of both the new and the old. For brevity we shall call this the "brain-mind." We know that it has a "self-destruct button" in the phenomenon of suicide as well as a "self-protect" apparatus which has been given various names from the "instinct of self-preservation" to the "defenses of character-structure." From 1920-1927 Freud, never deserting his interest in the brain, began to speak of a "protective barrier" in the mind—protective of life-process itself—a barrier ruptured by the impact of "shell-shock." For a combination of reasons—his struggle with cancer of the jaw and the final rising tide of the Hitler-Jung forces—he could not proceed to develop the brilliant insights of *"Beyond the Pleasure Principle."* But he did note that the manner in which the "unconscious mind" operated had nothing to do with our usual sequential or chronologic concept of time.

In *The Growth Concept of Nervous Integration* (1949) in a last chapter entitled: "Time-Space and the Sense of Reality" I indicated again that while *the "conscious" acted like a chronologist, the unconscious acted like a relativist.* I showed there why a dream had to be a four-dimensional phenomenon dependent upon inner electron speeds approaching the speed of light. By 1956-1960, I began slowly to extend Freud's concept of a life-process "protective barrier." I indicated in various studies in dreams and in the arts (cf. *The Psycho-*

analyst and the Artist[4] in 1950) that this protective barrier contained in it the phenomena of *intuition* and indeed that it acted as if it were the "dream-canvas" itself discharging enormous quantities of tension both sexual and somatic in general. *As such it certainly functioned to maintain the integrity of life-process.*

Moreover, the pre-dream "spikes" in the electroencephalogram again indicated a sharp change in the biomagnetic fields of the cerebral cortex as though—as an analogy—electron speeds and their orbiting radii were suddenly increasing under the necessity of discharging tension. In more conventional chemical terms, it might be described as enormous increase in "resting potentials" of brain cortical cells.

Slowly it became clear, from all the facts, that this relativistically behaving dream-apparatus was a separate system of the brain transformations whose rhythmic structures (like architecture in motion) we call the "mind." By 1960, I had named this system the *paraconscious* to distinguish it from the other three systems of what Freud—and all psychiatrists and psychoanalysts since then—called the "mind." The paraconscious was different from the "conscious," the "unconscious," and what was presumed to be a "turnstyle" between them, the "preconscious." *All these systems Freud had shown were under the impress of the sexual energy of the body*—in addition to the ordinary nutrient energy by which body cell structure is maintained. Upon these three systems—conscious, preconscious and unconscious—sexual energy played like a lambent flame until it became "fixed" by investment into character structure and ways of seeing and feeling. This was the gist of the pain-pleasure principle.

Then in 1920 Freud suddenly saw "beyond the pleasure principle" in the small volume by that title. Something else—a life-process protective barrier existed.

In naming that "protective barrier" the paraconscious I did not mean primarily to suggest that this system had to do necessarily with the increasing phenomena of parapsychology, though Freud himself was intrigued by the idea that the mind had perhaps certain "telepathic" receivers.

No, the concept of the paraconscious though it includes alert-alarm and echo-mirror scanning devices connected to a "mixer" system (RAS) streaming toward the prefrontal and temporal lobes of the brain, was not a system proving the presence of "extra-sensory perception." But it was—to my way of thinking and in accord with my observations clinically—a monitoring brain-heart and body-brain system of a very special kind having unsuspected "computer-composer" functions active in all the creative sciences and arts of man. It thus also provided "insight."

But, most important, it acted as though—again in defiance of all "classical neurology"—as though it had contact with every cell in the body even though classically we are all taught that the internal organs have no direct or indirect representation in the human cortex except in the use of parallel routes—not of the involuntary nervous system— whereby pain can register.

However, as preceding studies in this series of "revolution in the body-mind" have indicated, there is every reason to believe that the heart-arterial system of the body can act as an "informer" by the altering of the predeterminants of imagery (cf. *The Image of the Heart*[5]—1956)

Or, in brief, *the paraconscious system makes possible direct body-mind contact, once we understand the relativistic and paramagnetic laws governing life-process pulsing and sentient growth.* Anyone who has had—as I have had—the experience of being able to discern *a cancer dream* forewarning the dreamer of the presence of cancer in the body before it makes itself felt or otherwise evident, will not need too much persuasion of the existence, within the body-brain-mind transformations, of laws that tie them all together in a manner essentially simple.

It is for this reason that I have quoted in the frontispiece the beautiful eloquence of the great mind of Albert Einstein (his 1933 Herbert Spencer Lecture at Oxford, England):

> "Our experience up to date justifies us in feeling sure that in Nature is actualized the ideal of mathematic simplicity. It is my conviction that pure mathematic construction enables us to discover the concepts and the laws connecting them which give us the key to the understanding of the phenomena of Nature. . .

* * *

To summarize and rephrase the three major concepts upon which the equations presented here rest:

(1) Life-process is always life-process growth pulsing, sentient and genderizing. It depends upon the presence of "electron clockwork"— really the phenomenon of the energy levels of electrons which are free to move in a magnetic field from one energy level to another,—a phenomenon known to modern physics as EPR or electron paramagnetic resonance.

(2) For every species and for every individual male and female of that species, the moment of fertilization is the moment of the establishment (in however primordial a way) of the brain-heart design

and proportion unique to that unique individual in that unique species. Life-process growth pulsing, sentient and genderizing, is the growth of the body which will serve and obey the vital necessities to keep that pulsing and that sentience in optimum condition. The cells of the body are "tooled" to obey the brain-heart center by hypothalamic-pituitary and other devices, so that the EPR in the body cells of each species stands in a specific ratio to the heart's pulse, as will be demonstrated in the second and sixth of the equations. From this point of view hormones must now be seen not as "messengers," but as resident delegates, refurbished and re-supplied, ensuring that the biomagnetic fields of the cells are "orchestrated" by the "baton" of the heart-brain central control. This view will demand also a new concept of what an artery is and may elucidate why the arteries of coronary heart attack, of cerebral stroke, of certain forms of renal hypertension, and of senile dementia are usually injured *upstream* to the tissue—just before the "capillary bridge."

(3) The development of the concept of "the mind" is also integrated with the first two ideas in a new way. It is more correct to speak—in our modern world of physics—of brain-mind transforma-tions creating a dynamic structure not unlike "architecture in motion" and to consider all the evidence for a brain-heart monitoring system developed from Freud's original concept of a life-process "protective barrier" which I have renamed *the paraconscious*, as I have developed it. To this system are assigned the relativistic phenomena of dreams without the discharge of which—if sleep is prevented for three to four 24 hour periods—psychosis will occur. From man's capacity to dream emerge his arts and his sciences. But most important the paraconscious appears to have contact with every cell in the body as is foreshadowed in the increasing evidence of the "cancer dream" as well as of danger to the heart. This is made possible by the heart-arterial system's ability to change imagery-determinants and so to influence the curious "computer-composer" versatility of the paraconscious in the net "print-out" it provides both in dreams and in our intuitions. Its functions go *beyond* the sexual pain-pleasure principle but do not exclude the special nature of psychosexual energy transactions.

* * *

2. The Analogies to Modern Physics

Analogies are devices used to move from the known either to the unknown or the as yet imperfectly known. As more and more facts and experience with the imperfectly known begin to whittle down the degree of imperfection in our knowledge, the less analogy is needed and finally it "withers away."

While I am forced to use analogy here, I do not mean to imply that it is necessarily as far-fetched as it could appear to be. I do believe that the phenomena of *bio*physics are much more coherent with physics and mathematics than is generally permitted or admitted. In any event, as time goes on and more work is done, the realities will in any event appear and assert themselves, no matter how much fantasy one must suspect in one's self as one moves in the jungle of the unknown.

These are the major analogies used here:

(a) Plasma and Cyto-plasm The word "plasma" has long usage in medicine, e.g. as in blood plasma and cellular plasma or cytoplasm. But in modern thermonuclear physics it has a very precise and quite other meaning than a mixture of various ingredients essentially of cells, chemicals and fluids.

In modern "plasma physics" it means an assembly of ions, electrons, neutral atoms, and molecules in which the motion of the particles is *dominated by electromagnetic interactions.* A plasma itself is effectively neutral. Because a plasma is a conductor it interacts with electromagnetic fields. The science devoted to these interactions is known as hydromagnetics or magnetohydrodynamics.*

Our equations are based on analogous concepts—*as if* cyto-plasm—the stuff of cells—interacted with electromagnetic field forces . . . I believe that this is more fact than analogy but a discussion as to how valid this assumption is would take us too far afield here. It is quite obvious that life-process growth pulsing, sentient and genderizing, would have to make a totally effective control of body temperature imperative—and in modern physics the temperatures could never be coherent—in its machinery and its instruments with life-process growth requirements. The mechanisms by which life-process growth *could* become a science of *bio*hydromagnetics are to some degree known but not yet, to my knowledge, feasible.

Nevertheless, it would be impossible for the DNA-RNA mechanism to function without the presence of biomagnetic fields.

In addition to its domination by electromagnetic interactions, a plasma is capable of supporting various modes of vibration and can propagate several types of waves—these are the subject of the branch of plasma physics that is called "plasma oscillations" usually classified by their oscillation frequency.

In this work such oscillations are part and parcel of the analogic basis upon which the premises have been constructed.

This leads us to what I have called "electronic clockwork"—my

*"Brain Interactions With Weak Electric and Magnetic Fields" is the subject of the "Neurosciences Research Program Bulletin" Vol. 15, No. 1, January 1977, MIT Press—in which R. Wever points out that arcadian rhythms are generated by self-sustaining oscillators or internal clocks.

own catch-phrase for electronic paramagnetic resonance which is directly used in practically all the equations to be listed next. While EPR is by no means used here as mere analogy, I have included it under this heading in part as an introduction to the equations themselves but also because it implies the presence of a bioplasma such as is described above.

(b) Electron Paramagnetic Resonance. Our analogy is based upon the concept that there are in each cell thousands if not hundreds of thousands of paramagnetic field phenomena in action every second of our lives, even though field-intensity is very small.

Recall that the electron is a spinning charged particle which undergoes transitions between energy levels produced by the action of a magnetic field. These electron transitions are readily measured when the electron is unpaired. Their spectra (established and measured in spectroscopy) are used to study and measure the nature and concentrations of atoms, molecules, free radicals and other quantities. By virtue of its charge and spin an electron behaves like a bar magnet and can interact with an external magnetic field. In a group of free electrons, each electron is a magnetic dipole of a magnitude called the *Bohr magneton* after Niels Bohr. Its symbol is μ which amounts to 9.2732 x 10^{-21} ergs per gauss (gauss being a measure of the magnetic field strength measured by the symbol H). *Depending upon the direction of the electron's spin either toward or opposite to the magnetic field its energy will decrease (toward) or increase (opposite away). In most of the equations here, field strength (H) is taken as unity or 1 except as noted.**

Now there is an *electromagnetic radiation frequency* (a matter important to cancer research) frequently associated with the difference in energy of "toward" and "opposite away" and which will satisfy the equation:

Difference in Energy = $h\nu$ = (g=2.0029) x (μ = 9.2732 ergs/gauss) x H_{gauss}

in which h is Planck's constant = 6.625 x 10^{-27} erg-sec. and g is the *gyromagnetic constant*, ordinarily equal to 2 but in a free electron due to relativity effects = 2.00229. Solving for ν in the $h\nu$ above results in the value 2.8026 x 10^6 cycles per sec per gauss. This frequency is capable of causing energy level transitions depending upon the magnetic field strength H.

*The entire earth's magnetic field is only about $1/2$ gauss. And, the biomagnetic value for physiologic processes is one-billionth of that or, approximately, 0.5 x 10^{-9}. In our concept, this means that a constant of approximately 2 x 10^9 is in operation resulting in the steady *mathematic* finding of 1 gauss in all the equations except as noted varying slightly in Equation VII (or 2 x 10^9 x 0.5 x 10^{-9} = 1). This means that the *paramagnetic* interacting fields are the result of a "swarm of free electrons" in piezoelectric transformations in constant life-process oscillatory motion.

In this work we treat that EPR electromagnetic radiation frequency and the Bohr magneton as basic constants, as will appear in the listing of and brief comments on the equations.

Let us summarize then the nature of the "analogy" thus far.

We assume the presence of a "bioplasma" composed of ions, electrons, neutral atoms and molecules—a bioplasma dominated by electromagnetic interactions *which are fundamental to the chemistry* of both nucleus DNA and cytoplasmic RNA "commuting" from nucleus to ribosome. This bioplasma is capable of stability and also of supporting vibrations and even of propagating waves of several frequencies. The "brain-wave" (alpha and other frequencies are examples) and the "heart-wave" better known as the electro-cardiogram can be considered as two different frequencies indicating that the living body has not merely one "pulse"—the "heart-beat"—but that it is a composite of several pulsing systems, perhaps a different frequency for each of the seven major body tissue systems. In the listing and brief comments appended to each, Equation II for man and Equation VI for various species rests upon this concept:—that there is an oscillating frequency parameter for each species in the ratio of total body-cell oscillation in relation to the heart-pulse. It will be seen there that for man the ratio of heart to body pulse is 1:10,000.

These then are *the equations of the science of the bioplasma.* In the form presented here it is original with me as are the equations. But before we go to the "mathematic proof of the pudding," there is one more analogy that must be incorporated in our laying a foundation for the science of the bioplasma. This is the bioplasma formulation for what has been called "resistance to growth" in every cell—a resistance which normally imposes normal limits upon its size and numbers so that it knows "when and where to stop" in the intricate but beautifully timed architectural design of the pulsing, sentient, and genderizing body. *Its importance in cancer is obvious* but the actual nature of that "resistance to growth" has been veiled in mystery. (It was first described in the brilliant papers of Wetzel. "On the Motion of Growth" forty-four years ago (1932); however Wetzel's work[6] was based on Newtonian analogy with no primary interest in heart, brain or "bioplasma" electromagnetic considerations.) Moreover the "resistance to growth" will play a crucial role in heat-production; and, in cancer the local tissue heat-production appears to fall, as does the resistance to growth which would otherwise limit it. Another analogy from plasma and magnetic physics falls into place here.

The final component of our bioplasma analogy is that which in physics is called the *magnetic mirror effect*. Its great importance to heat and growth regulation—so important to cancer—will at once be obvious.

When charged particles are moving in a magnetic field and certain conditions ensuring neither heat-gain nor heat-loss are established (*adiabatic* conditions), then the particle *magnetic moment* (having to do with the rotation and direction of the particle in relation to the magnetic field) and the *kinetic energy* will become constants of the motion.*

In simple terms the motion and heat production will be stabilized. Under these conditions as the particle moves along a magnetic line of force it will meet a maximum field where it will no longer have any velocity-along-the-line, (translation velocity). All of its kinetic energy is then associated with rotational motion and "reflecting" then occurs. (The particle "spins in place"—is an approximate way of stating the matter—and in controlled thermonuclear reactors this effect is used to confine a high temperature plasma in a cylindrical magnetic field.)

While there is no basis for any analogy to high temperature thermonuclear reactors, there is *a priori* no reason why a similar restraining and confining effect—if not the identical one—could not exist in a "bioplasma," with very extensive modifications.

The concept then of a bioplasma—if validated—would bring considerable *order* to the present chaos meant by the term "life-process"—any volume about which will present one with chapters covering DNA, enzymes, proteins, genetic codes, the genetics of bacteria and viruses, regulatory mechanisms, immunity, hormones, cell membranes, and an entire gallery of different points of view of whatever researcher's point of view happens to serve the purpose of the "chapter." Such books ask the apparently "logical questions" such as: "Why is it that the mouse lives only about 400-600 days while the elephant may live for fifty years or more?"—even though the individual cells of both species are very similar. All kinds of theories have been advanced without any awareness of the possibility of specific heart-brain-body ratios of oscillating frequencies in each species—cf. Equation VI and Figure 6. By orienting one's questioning merely to the "similarity" in the way cells *look* and to the catalogue of their ingredients, one gets no answers, only more theories.

The proposed science of a fundamental bioplasma—interested in our "electron clockwork"—so important to heart and brain—asks instead a first question in the longevity mystery:

(1) How many heart beats do we live?

*Cf. in *Neurosciences Research Program Bulletin*—footnote pg. 28—the report by W. A. Little who describes (pg. 63) the conditions under which the energy of brain tissue interaction with electromagnetic fields would be proportional to the number of molecules in a crystal-like "swarm" arrangement.

Cf. also report by K. H. Illinger with reference to the perturbations by an electromagnetic field including the energy of an isolated molecule separable into electronic, vibrational and rotational degrees of freedom.

Species	Life-Span (in Minutes)/		Heart-Pulse/Min.	Total
Mouse	500 x 24 x 60 = 720,000 (at 600 days)	x	700	5.04×10^8 6.05×10^8
Whale	75 x 365 x 24 x 60 = 39,420,000 (Whales may live much longer than 75 years.) (at 100 years)	x	10	3.942×10^8 5.256×10^8
Elephant	50 x 365 x 24 x 60 = 26,280,000 (at 35 years)	x	30	7.884×10^8 5.519×10^8
Man	70 x 365 x 24 x 60 = 36,792,000 (at 50 years)	x	76	2.796×10^9 1.99728×10^9

Or, in other words, the moment we approach the matter of life-process as *life-process growth pulsing and sentient* and as a *bioplasma capable of supporting and propagating oscillating frequencies in species-specific heart-body ratios* we begin to get answers which surprisingly indicate that the mouse lives "longer-heart-beats" than the whale—and if the elephant in the example above lives only say 35 years instead of 50, then his "heart-beat-span" is *only 5.519 x 10⁸—not much more fortunate than our little mouse*!

The second question which we ask from our point of view is of course *what the brain-heart ratio is* for this too is species-specific—being greatest in man. And this second question shifts the issue from "length of years" to the important question of relative and absolute *power* differences in the various species.

* * * * * * * *

We shall now proceed to the equations which, as I have said, are for me the "proof of the pudding"—a proof to which I have devoted a great many hours almost from the beginning of my professional life—for over forty years beginning with *The Growth Concept of Nervous Integration* (1936-1949).;

In later reports each of the equations will form a separate "chapter." Here they are merely listed with very brief comment. (An appendix devotes space to the more detailed discussion and derivation of Equation I—The "Relativity Equation.")*

I publish them in this form out of the sense of urgency in the challenge of the disasters of cancer, psychosis, heart attack and stroke, and the arthritides in each of which there is a different assault upon the integrity of life-process bioplasma.

* * * * * * * *

Equation I: The "Relativity Equation."

Various considerations suggested that if brain-heart controlled the bioplasma of the body, then there ought to exist a formulation for

*Cf. Note 2 in Appendix.

life-process growth which would approach the Einsteinian mass-energy equivalence law.* Using the formulation of Coulomb's law, we arrived at a net result which stated:

$$0.040188 \times Brain_{gms.} \times Heart_{gms.} \times \frac{Catecholamine\ Ratio}{gram} = Living\ Body\ Wt._{gms.}$$

We had already established the constant of maintenance 0.040188, in the brain weight, the heart weight and the body weight by other means to be described in the equations that follow. Our purpose was to solve for the ratio of the breakdown products of dopamine and the adrenalines. The former is homovanillic acid (HVA), the latter are metanephrine (M) and normetanephrine (NM). We found sharp agreement in the results for the HVA:M+NM ratio as compared with the careful study by Gitlow *et al*[7]. Table I shows the total picture of the equation and Table I(A) shows the objective HVA:M+NM ratio in comparison with our derived results. Figure 1 shows the results of Equation I (in company with the results of Equation II). The appendix will supply the full derivation of Equation I.

Equation II: The "Paramagnetic Equation."

Equation II derives from Equation I. In order to establish the main link, it is necessary to know that the constant 0.040188 of Equation I contains the electromagnetic frequency value of 2.8026 x 10^6 cycles per sec per gauss. The equation is called "paramagnetic" because of its dependence upon the electron paramagnetic resonance phenomena already discussed.

Equation II states:

$$\frac{\frac{4\pi}{3}[r^3 = (\frac{1}{2}L)^3]\ [Pulse\ freq.\ \times 10^4\ cycles\ per\ sec\ per\ gauss]\ [\frac{Brain_{gms.-18y}}{Heart_{gms-18y}}] = Body\ Wt._{gms.}}{2.8026 \times 10^6\ cycles\ per\ sec\ per\ gauss}$$

Figure 1 shows—in company with the body weight of Equation I—the results in body weight. Table II shows the results of Equation II and since body length and brain and heart weights are available, the pulse/sec may be derived from the "Body EPR" value above given as Pulse freq. x 10^4 cycles per sec. per gauss. A specific gravity of 1 is assumed for the first volume variable.

(As already discussed, Equation VI states the same equation as Equation II but only for the adults of the various species and Figure 6 illustrates the bioplasma life-process phenomena of "heart-beat-life-span"—the main ordinate is organized on the plan of adult heart-beat

*Of interest in this connection is Szent-Györgyi's concept of an "electron biology" in which electrons and photons interact to produce the brown-colored proteins of living tissue. (cf. note 7 in the Appendix)

TABLE I

Age (years)	Calculated Brain Weight gms. (Product) gms²	x Calculated Heart Weight gms.	Calculated Catecholamine Ratio/gram x 0.040188	Calculated Body Weight gms.	Empiric Body Weight gms. (Geigy Docum.)	Wetzel Series Body Weight gms.
Birth	379.53 (9226.3743)	24.31	0.37284	3440	3380	3250
½	726.10 (24781.79930)	34.13	0.30506	7560	7420	7570
1	904.72 (39807.6800)	44.00	0.25272	10060	9910	10060
2	1007.27 (58472.0235)	58.05	0.21344	12480	12430	12700
3	1120.19 (74100.5685)	66.15	0.19853	14711	14520	15040
4	1158.64 (92065.5340)	79.46	0.181827	16740	16470	16710
6	1245.13 (130439.8100)	104.76	0.165256	21566	21530	20450
8	1265.13 (168945.4602)	133.54	0.15903	26867	26810	26340
10	1310.74 (207962.1084)	158.66	0.1569035	32630	32250	32530
12	1345.11 (235421.1522)	175.02	0.165643	38996	39010	38680
15	1345.34 (335514.3426)	249.39*	0.15588	52300	52950	14 years: 48620 / 16 years: 56000
18	1345.24 (367815.5208)	273.42	0.16736	61556	58720	63000

*The more correct value here may be 249.38 with a corresponding value for the Catecholamine Ratio x 0.040188 = 0.155889.

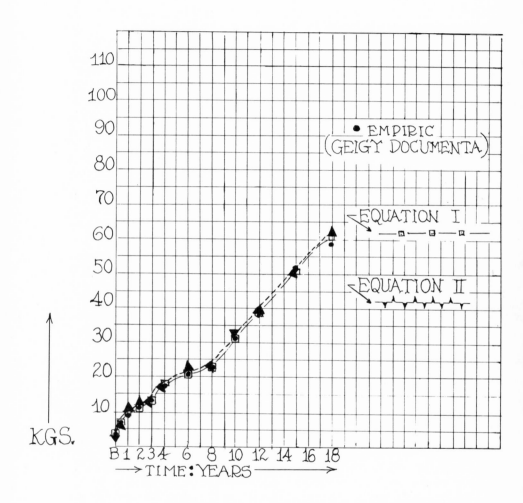

FIG.1:HUMAN BODY GROWTH

CALCULATED BY RELATIVISTIC EQUATION I

AND BY·PARAMAGNETIC(EPR) EQUATION II

TABLE I (A)

Age (years)	Calculated Catecholamine Ratio (x 0.040188) per gram	Empiric HVA/M+NM ratio (x 0.040188)	Empiric HVA/M+NM ratio (in g/mg creatinine)	Body Weight (grams) using empiric Cate Factor	Body Weight (grams) calc. from Table 1
Birth	0.372844	0.31619 0.36786	*12.9:1.64 **15.0:1.64	3354	3440
6 mos.	0.30506	0.30875	12.6:1.68	7652	7560
1	0.25272	0.24352	7.58:1.25	9714	10060
2	0.21344	-----	------	----	12480
3	0.⌄9853	-----	------	----	14711
4	0.181827	-----	------	----	16740
(5-10 years)					
6	0.16533	0.16714	4.70:1.13	21897	21566
8	0.15903	-----	------	-----	26867
10	0.1569035	0.16702	2.50:0.60	34730	32630
12	0.165643	-----	------	-----	38996
(15-18 years)					
15	0.15588	0.16578	1.00:0.24	-----	52300
18	0.16736	0.16578	1.00:0.24	60979	61556

Notes: (1): *Estimated for newborns. Values may oscillate wildly above
　　　　**12.9

(2) ------- no data yet available

per minute for each species—in relation to body weight and to brain-heart ratio for both terrestrials and aquatics.)

So far as I know Equation II determines the pulse of man (and all higher forms) on the basis of coherent theory for the first time. Figure 3 shows the reciprocal relationship between pulse and empiric length. Table 3 shows the calculation of "ideal length" on this basis.

But we now—in addition to this brief listing—must make certain minimum comments on some of the consequences—the bioplasma consequences—of Equations I and II.

First let us state Equation II in an even more simplified form in which it is possible to see its constant as 2.8026×10^6 cycles per sec per

TABLE II

AGE (years)	MASS(1)* (gms.) MASS(2)**	$\times 2.8026 \times 10^2$	Pulse per sec	½L (cms.)	BRAIN: HEART RATIO	$r^3\ _{cms.}{}^3$ $\times 4.18879$ $\times 4.92$
Birth	3440 — 3436.79	964094	2.92	25.2	4.92	16003.01 67033.25 329,803.59
½	7560 — 7515.57	2118766	2.89	32.9	4.92	35611.29 149168.71 733907.59
1	10060 — 10076.74	2819416	2.63	37.35	4.92	52104.09 218253.09 1073805.2
2	12480 — 12494.70	3497645	2.06	43.53	4.92	82483.29 345505.19 1699885.5
3	14711 — 14701.17	4122904.8	1.81	47.98	4.92	110453.81 462667.81 2276325.6
4	16740 — 16718.12	4691552.4	1.65	51.65	4.92	137787.36 577164.41 2839648.8
6	21556 — 21621.03	6041284.5	1.48 (1.4755)	58.35	4.92	198665.55 832168.26 4094267.8
8	26867 — 26835.56	7529745.4	1.36	64.5	4.92	268336.12 1124003.6 5530097.7
10	32630 — 32660.50	9144883.8	1.31	69.73	4.92	339046.28 1420193.6 6987352.5
12	38996 — 38896.38	10929018	1.27	74.68	4.92	416498.00 1744622.6 8583543.1
15	52300 — 52096.95	14657598	1.27	82.32	4.92	557848.25 2336709.2 11496609
18	61556 — 61,858.21	17251684	1.26	87.40***	4.92	667627.62 2796551.8 13759034

MASS (1)* is the beginning mass value in grams used to determine pulse.

MASS (2)** is the mass value recalculated after the pulse has been determined.

87.40*** is the value of the radius at 18 years in contrast to 84.25 cms. due to the unusual increment in torso and width at this age making the "radius" greater by 3.15 cms.

gauss in relation to brain-heart ratio at 18 years of age (= 4.92) and to the species specific coefficient for man (= 10^4 or 10,000). Thus, Equation II may also be written:

$$\frac{2.8026 \times 10^6 \text{ cycles/sec/g.}}{4.18879 \times 4.92 \times 10^4} \times \frac{\text{Body Weight}_{gms.}}{\text{Pulse/sec/gauss}} = r^3 = (\text{½ Body Length})^3_{cm^3}$$

This resolves into

$$13.59894* \times \frac{\text{Body Weight}_{gms.}}{\text{Pulse}_{numerical\ value}} = r^3 = (\text{½ Body Length})^3_{cm^3}$$

Equation II in this form expresses clearly the role of the electromagnetic frequency of EPR in the synthesis of body weight in relation to body length and to the *limiting brain:heart (at 18 years) value and its* associated 10^4 coefficient for body:heart "pulsing." We take this again as clear evidence of a bioplasma capable of supporting and propagating oscillations of varied and specific frequencies limited by the brain:heart forces of the particular species.

Now, let us turn back to Equation I and study the important phenomena illustrated in Figures 2-A and 2-B.

* * * * * * * *

The thrust of the transformation of the Catecholamine Ratio into three major frequencies of life-process growth is contained in Figures 2-A and 2-B. The first—Figure 2-A—illustrates the calculated versus the empiric Catecholamine Ratio multiplied by the constant 0.040188. Equation I achieved this result, it will be remembered by using previously established brain, heart, and body weight in a manner still to be described below.

Our next step was to equate this *product* with the relationship of heart-beat (pulse frequency) to alpha frequency of the EEG and to another *as yet unknown* oscillating frequency in the numerator of the formulation:

$$0.040188 \frac{\text{(HVA)}}{\text{(M+NM)gm.}} = \frac{\text{Pulse/sec + G.F.f.}}{\text{(alpha frequency) grams}}$$

the results of which are charted in Figure 2-B. In brief, in the bioplasma we consider that at least three major frequencies (and

---

*Cf. Note 6 in the Appendix where the constant is derived on the basis of a mirror-image symmetry—as our original constant for bioplasma synthesizing gravitational interaction.

TABLE III

Age (years)	Body Weight (grams)	Pulse per sec.	½ Body Length Empiric–Calculated (cms.)		r^3 Empiric (cms.^{3})	r^3 Calculated (cms.^{3})
Birth	3440	2.92	25.2	25.307 (50.614)	16003.01	16020.668
½	7560	2.89	32.9	32.569 (65.138)	35611.29	35573.695
1	10060	2.63	37.35	37.338 (74.676)	52104.09	52017.235
2	12480	2.06	43.53	43.514 (87.028)	82483.29	82385.810
3	14711	1.81	47.98	47.904 (95.808)	110453.81	110527.070
4	16740	1.65	51.65	51.670 (103.340)	137787.36	137967.420
6	21556	1.4755	58.35	58.350 (116.600)	198665.55	198670.780
8	26867	1.36	64.5	64.52 (116.700)	268336.12	268649.050
10	32630	1.31	69.73	69.71 (139.420)	339046.28	338727.790
12	38996	1.27	74.68	74.738 (149.476)	416498.00	417562.400
15	52300	1.27	82.32	82.442 (164.884)	557848.25	560019.330
18	61556	1.26	87.40	87.250 (174.500)	667627.62	664362.180
**18	61556	**1.2519	87.40	87.44 (174.880)	****667627.62	668660.71**

**The sensitivity of the result is indicated by an alternate pulse of 1.2519 per sec. as compared with 1.26 per sec.

****The "ideal pulse" at 18 years corresponding to 667627.62 cms.^{3} would be 1.25383782, if it were at all possible to measure it to so fine a point.

Note:

  Body Length takes on a new significance in these studies in view of our equations being in part based upon the length of each base pair of the double helix (or $3.4 A^o$).

probably a great many more) are being supported and propagated.

  We have called this frequency the "Gender Force factor" or the G.F.f. Figure 2-B illustrates the fact that—mathematically—it is *negative* until 4-6 years of age. Thereafter it becomes positive and may increase slightly and rather slowly—by our present calculations—until 32 years of age when all growth finally comes to its equilibrating end. (The skull apparently grows until that age.)

  The importance of the Gender Force factor is very large. To my knowledge it has never been discovered or described before.

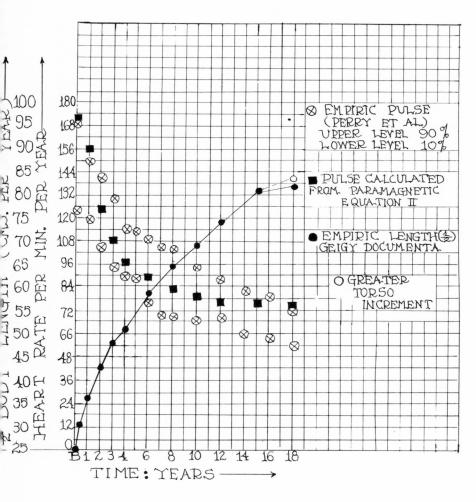

FIG. 3: HUMAN PULSE RATE
CALCULATED FROM PARAMAGNETIC EQUATION II
AS RATIO OF 1:10,000 OF BODY CYCLES/SEC/G
IN RELATION TO ½ LENGTH AS BODY RADIUS

First, it is quite clear that the larger and the more positive it is—up to 32 years of age—the greater will be the body weight. The lesser and the more diminished it is in the positive phase after 6 years of age, the smaller the body weight will be. *The larger value at its limit will produce the male weight curve. The smaller value at its limit will produce the female weight curve.* Hence we have used the term "Gender" to describe its place in the bioplasma scheme of things.

Second, and even more intriguing, is the fact of its "negativity" until 4-6 years of age. *This can only mean an increasing energy direction.* It raises the important question: Is this a "set" of "gender electrons" in the bioplasma spinning in the "toward" direction of a "genderizing" paramagnetic field?

Table V shows all the variables including the increments in the G.F.f. and its percentage increment each year. This latter set of values is charted in Figure 5 where it is set against the illustrative background of the percentage growth of the endocrines and the male incidence of schizophrenia.

But Figure 5 (we are forced to anticipate here) not only illustrates the dramatic correlation of the G.F.f. in its "percentage growth" form with the bulk of the male age-incidence curve (actually as we know a very few cases may be present at birth), but even more it fully and entirely confirms all the work of Freud and all studies in the psychodynamics of both schizophrenia *and homosexuality.* For, it is between 4-6 years of age that the *identification* process—*the gender-identification process* is rivetted into place.

Since we know that homosexuality is a brain-mind disease—homosexuality has been called a "way-station" on the road to a possible schizophrenic "break"—what we see in Figure 5 as it charts the percentage growth factor of Gender Force is the "turn around"—the change in direction—of the biomagnetic forces in the bioplasma establishing gender and final and firm gender-direction.

Thus—to anticipate Equation V to which we will devote additional attention when we reach that point on our "list"—we can write for now:

$$\text{alpha frequency} \left(0.040188 \frac{HVA}{(M+NM)\text{gms.}} \right) - \text{Pulse/sec} = \text{G.F.f.}$$

Equation III (A). The Equation of Species Characteristics

To resume our listing in proper order, it is now possible to equate Equation I and Equation II. For brevity I have called this the

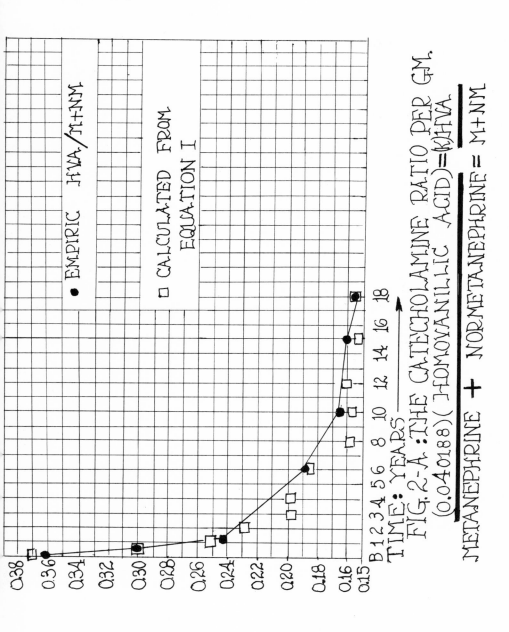

• EMPIRIC HVA/M+NM

□ CALCULATED FROM EQUATION I

TIME: YEARS

FIG. 2-A : THE CATECHOLAMINE RATIO PER GM.

$$\frac{(0.040188)(\text{HOMOVANILLIC ACID})=(k)HVA}{\text{METANEPHRINE} + \text{NORMETANEPHRINE} = M+NM}$$

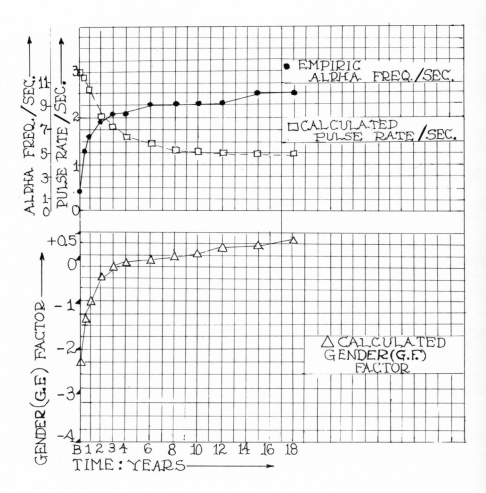

FIG.2-B: BIOMAGNETIC FACTORS

EQUAL TO (K)HVA/M+NM OF FIG 2-A

"equation of species characteristics." It might have been called the "equation of species bioplasma characteristics."

Taking the second and simplified form of Equation II, we may write: *(Equating I and II)*

$$0.040188 \ (\text{Brain x Heart})_{gms}{}^2 \ \frac{\text{x Cate. Ratio}}{\text{gram}} = \frac{r^3 \ (=\tfrac{1}{2} \text{ Body L})^3 \ \text{x Pulse/sec}}{13.59894}{}_{n.v.}$$

and therefore **Equation III:**

$$\frac{(\text{Brain x Heart})_{gms.}{}^2 \ \text{x Cate. Ratio/gm.}}{r^3 \ \text{x Pulse/sec}_{n.v.}} = \frac{0.0735351}{0.040188} = 1.8297775$$

(n.v. is *numerical value*) (r³ denotes *grams*, as function of vol. x sp.gr.)

We are not aware of any theoretically coherent theory embracing all these variables as simply and as clearly.

* * * * * * * *

The Cancer Loss of Weight As a Dissociation of the Relationship Between Bioplasma Oscillation Frequency and the Frequencies of Brain-Wave and Heart-Pulse.

Our listing of the equations must be briefly interrupted here by a consideration of Equations I, II and III which clearly and simply illustrate what would happen if there were a "schizophrenia of the body"—i.e. a dissociation of the bioplasma normal frequency in relation to the pulse. We know *for a fact* that all indications are that cancer cells operate out of "low resting potentials" and can be destroyed if they can be reached by electromagnetic radiation frequency because they can not stand the temperature gradients which can be endured by normal tissue.

Examine the formation of the constant 13.59894, where

$$\frac{2.8026 \times 10^6 \ \text{cycles/sec/g.}}{4.18879 \times 4.92 \times 10^4 \ \text{cycles/sec/g.}} = 13.59894$$

the cycles/sec/g. cancelling out.

What happens if the quantity ($10^4 = 10,000$) is *reduced* for the entire body to say 6000?

Using the second and simplified form of Equation II (as Equation III), and solving for body weight at any year, pulse for the corresponding year, and a corresponding length—say at birth—the result is, with r³ = 16003.01 and pulse at 2.92, *a body weight of 2061.7136 grams instead of 3440 grams.*

Of course this would represent cancer in the total body—cancer rampant and incredibly invasive. *But before that end-stage precisely the same dissociation would be functioning in the cancer-initiating tissue.*

It is the detection and measurement of this phenomenon which requires the science of the bioplasma.

Equation IV, A, B, C: The Bioplasma's Basic "Template" (Basic Tissue-Differentiating Mass—TDM)

On the "landscape" of the bioplasma of every cell—dominated by the interactions of electromagnetic fields—we know there are the "magic mountains" of the double helix, as well as the "rivers" along which the RNA is "carried" by electrophoretic vehicles. We know too how the "magic mountains" code, instruct, and transmit *via* transfer RNA the message for manufacture in the "industrial valleys" of the ribosome. We know that from the very first moment of fertilization "programs" appear to—*first*—synthesize the basic tissue of the first daughter cells, and—*second*—to begin the differentiation-stage at which the basic tissue will be modified so that the cells of each different—but co-operating—system will be structured for its function.

We do not yet know the *signalling system* by which cells of one tissue "send" to another. Here, in the science of the bioplasma we may be able to offer some leads. This will be particularly evident in our new concept of the artery, and of cell membranes as "reponders."

But the phenomenon of cloning tells us that in any cell there exists even in the completed adult the basic potential for the original program so that the insertion of an adult cell nucleus into an ovum with nucleus extirpated can start the entire process over again to produce an exact copy of the adult. The copy is the clone.

To locate and to measure the basic tissue differentiating mass (TDM$_{basic}$) would then enable us to make such modifications in our equations for each tissue as enormously to simplify the picture of the growth of the systems. It would also enable us to have a better picture of what happens when growth reaches its practical equilibrium and tissue cells all over the body would have to be able to replenish the cells destroyed, e.g. the refurbishment of blood cells. And this TDM we would designate as TDM$_{lpm}$ the *lpm* meaning *life-process maintenance.* For example at 18 years of age we have determined that this amount is 727.59 grams in relation to the total body weight of 61556 grams, the ratio having the value of 0.01182. When this is multiplied by 3.4, the numerical value in Angström of the length of each base pair of the double helix, the result is the constant of Equation I or 0.040188.

Our approach to the determination of TDM_{basic} meant that, if successful, we could then build the equations for brain, heart, cord, body and gender-genital mass upon that foundation. It would mean of course that each of the tissue cells would have its own "growth resistance" (when and where does the growth of a cell stop?) and this we have already indicated is also biomagnetic as already detailed in the analogy to the magnetic mirror effect. To considerable degree this is expressed in the length and width of the total body.

Furthermore it was fairly clear that the TDM_{basic} as well as the individual shaping of each cell and tissue would reflect the spiral structure of the double helix as modified by individual magnetic mirror effects. And, the basic strucure would be segmental and segmentally fused. The spinal cord then was the tissue with which we would start to derive the TDM_{basic}, and we would use a modified equation of the spiral: (Equation IV)

$$0.01\pi(TDM)_{basic} -0.02e(dL)(dW)_h + R_{gc} + \pi = Cord_{gms.} \times Spir. Exp. = Body\ Wt._{gms.}{}^*$$

We would use empiric data to solve for the TDM_{basic} and then recalculate to discover the specific growth resistance for the cord (R_{gc}). If we were correct in our assumptions, then the total body weight would be reflected in a spiral exponential relationship to the segmental organization of the cord.

We would later have other methods to be shown below to confirm our determination of the TDM_{basic}. Our first step was to average a series of cord weights, and from this to establish the exponential relation to body weight (also averaged from various series). Then we would "match" our spinal cord equation to the empiric series, and approximate "growth resistance" at first based on our early work in 1949 and so solve finally for TDM_{basic}.

The results for TDM_{basic} were as follows:

Birth	142.30 grams	*6 yrs.*	365.77 grams
½ yr.	186.90 "	*8 yrs.*	441.00 "
1 yr.	224.20 "	*10 yrs.*	498.40 "
2 yrs.	267.82 "	*12 yrs.*	556.50 "
3 yrs.	272.00 "	*15 yrs.*	681.76 "
4 yrs.	297.46 "	*18 yrs.*	727.59 "

*L is body length (total), W is pelvic width, R_{gc} is growth resistance of cord tissue.

The results for the relationship of the spinal cord to the body weight were as follows:

Age (Years)	Spinal Cord$_{gms.}$	Spiral Exponent	Body Wt.$_{gms.}$
Birth	3.82158	0.90015×10^3	3440
½	8.04127	0.94015×10^3	7560
1	10.263736	0.98015×10^3	10060
2	11.771959	1.06015×10^3	12480
3	12.902683	1.14015×10^3	14711
4	13.719624	1.22015×10^3	16740
6	15.618592	1.38015×10^3	21556
8	17.444404	1.54015×10^3	26867
10	19.192424	1.70015×10^3	32630
12	20.9639	1.86015×10^3	38996
15	24.902983	2.10015×10^3	52300
18	26.304296	2.34015×10^3	61556

Table IV shows the total results including comparison with the empiric data of the Geigy Documenta, and with the excellent studies of Wetzel[6]. In a similar manner brain weight was derived from precisely the same formulation except that the spiral exponent is "descending." These are the brain weights and body weights used in Equation I where, employing empiric Catecholamine Ratio values we could achieve a first statement of the values of the heart. But, as with the TDM_{basic}, so too with the heart. We have other methods available to confirm the values presented. (Cf. the first two columns of Table VIII for earlier derivations of brain weight and cord weight. Equation IX* is the ultimate brain weight derivation.)

Figures 4-A and 4-B show the results. Figure 4-B shows the brain, cord, heart and body weights achieved, in relation to TDM_{basic}. Figure 4-A shows that the TDM_{basic} can be considered to have two different fractions: a TDM minimum and constant value for life-process maintenance and a fraction we have called "growth-TDM" over and above that needed, beyond sheer life-process maintenance, to shape out the brain-heart values and the Catecholamine Ratio of the

*Cf Note 3 in Appendix.

TABLE IV

AGE years	*TDM$_{basic}$ grams	0.02e** dLxdW gms	R *** $\frac{cord}{gms}$	π	Cord Wt. grams	x	Spiral Exponent =	Calc. Body Wt. grams	Empiric Body Wt. grams (Geigy Doc.)	Wetzel Body Wt. grams
Birth	142.30	3.8314	0.04318	3.1416	3.82158	x	900.15	3440	3380	3250
½	186.90	1.0875	0.118166	3.1416	8.04127	x	940.14	7560	7420	7570
1	224.20	0.2023	0.280969	3.1416	10.263736	x	980.15	10060	9910	10060
2	267.82	0.1341	0.350626	3.1416	11.771959	x	1060.15	12480	12430	12700
3	272.00	0.0311	1.24703	3.1416	12.902683	x	1140.15	14711	14520	15040
4	297.46	0.0675	1.300521	3.1416	13.719624	x	1220.15	16740	16470	16710
6	365.77	0.0296	1.015562	3.1416	15.618592	x	1380.15	21556	21530	20450
8	441.00	0.0255	0.473848	3.1416	17.444404	x	1540.15	26867	26810	26340
10	498.40	0.0203	0.41339	3.1416	19.192424	x	1700.15	32630	32250	32530
12	556.50	0.0389	0.378196	3.1416	20.9639	x	1860.15	38996	39010	38680
15	681.76	0.0171	0.360311	3.1416	24.902983	x	2100.15	52300	52950	52310
18	727.59	0.0020	0.306420	3.1416	26.304296	x	2340.15	61556	59820	63000

*In the equation this becomes 0.01π TDM$_{basic}$.

**Actually this is cms^2 but is taken here as an approximation of volume x specific gravity = 1, or grams.

***R$_{cord\ gms.}$ is "Growth Resistance".

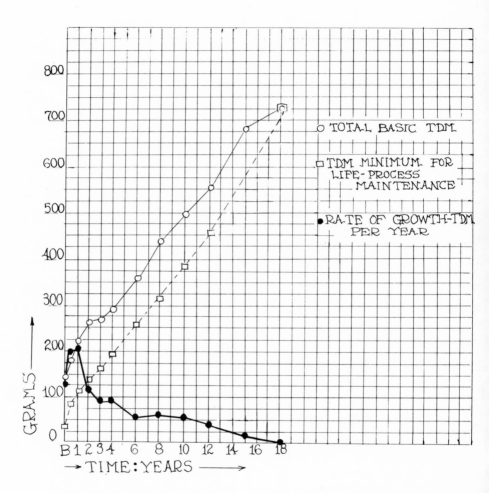

FIG. 4A: BASIC TDM GROWTH

TABLE IV (A)

Age Yrs.	Total Basic TDM (grams)	TDM_{lpm} (grams)	TDM_{bhgg} (grams)	RATE of TDM_{bhgg} per year
Birth	142.30	40.57333	101.72667	135.63556
½	186.90	89.16697	97.73303	195.46606
1	224.20	118.6534	105.5466	211.0932
2	267.80	147.19626	120.60374	120.60374
3	272.00	173.50996	98.49004	98.49004
4	297.46	197.44114	100.01886	100.01886
6	365.77	254.24381	111.52619	55.763095
8	441.00	316.88478	124.11522	62.05761
10	498.40	384.85691	113.54309	56.771545
12	556.50	459.94116	96.55884	48.27942
15	681.76	616.85615	64.90385	21.634616
18	727.59	726.02672	1.56328	0.5210933

species. The student of growth and of heat-production will recognize the similarity of the curve of "growth-TDM" to that of heat/kilo. It foreshadows our equation VII for the biomagnetic solution of heat-production obeying the characteristics of the bioplasma.

Equation IV (A). TDM_{Imp}:

If we now apply the constant 0.040188 in a new way, we can achieve the TDM_{Imp} for every age, as shown in Figure 4-A. Dividing the numerical value of the length of the double helix' single base pair—or 3.4—by 0.040188 we obtain the value 84.602368.

This is so close to our expected theoretic value—expected because of the biomagnetic characteristics of the bioplasma—that we intend to use the ideal value which is 84.784758. This is the sum of C^4—in sheer numerical terms—or 80.775593—plus the value for the *gyromagnetic* constant we saw earlier operating in the phenomenon of EPR, namely $g^2 = (2.00229)^2 = 4.0091652$. The sum of both is 84.784758.

The reason for using these established constant values will become apparent when we consider that the biomagnetic fields of the

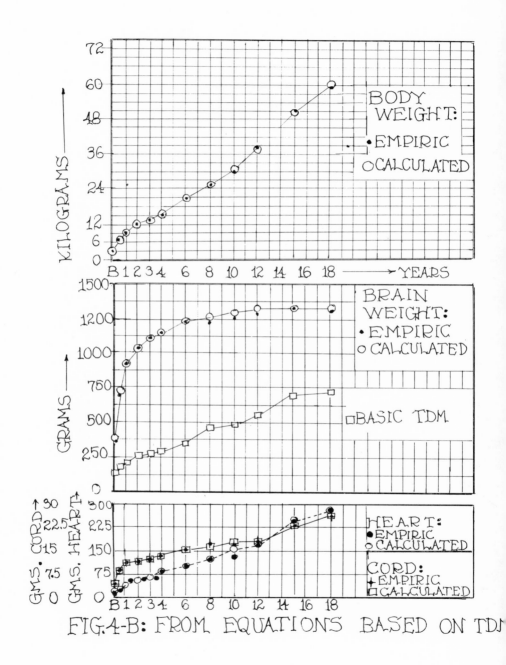

FIG. 4-B: FROM EQUATIONS BASED ON TDM

bioplasma must be treated as symmetrical, i.e. multiplied by each other or "squared" because of our structured mirror-image symmetry.

Applying this constant to every year of life, we obtain the TDM_{lmp} for every year, thus:

Birth: 84.784758 (TDM_{lpm}) = 3440 gms; TDM_{lpm} = 40.57333 gms.

½ yr.:   84.784758 (TDM_{lpm}) = 7560 gms; TDM_{lpm} = 89.16697 gms.

For the remainder of the determinations, consult Table IV (A) where the distinction is drawn between TDM_{lmp} and TDM_{bhgg} the subscript *bhgg* meaning brain-heart-gender growth.

We shall indicate later how $C^4 + g^2$ enter into the change in the biomagnetic fields of the bioplasma as myelinization is completed.

* * * * * * * *

Equation IV (B). Heart-Artery Equivalence to TDM_{basic}

It has been indicated that a new concept of the artery must accompany the concept of a bioplasma dominated as we have tried to show by interacting electromagnetic fields in a biologic-chemical medium usually in the past called the cellular "cytoplasm" but not meaning the same thing as the biologic "modification" of (really analogy to) modern plasma physics.

Here we begin to state that the artery is not a "pipeline" carrying blood, oxygen, metabolites, enzymes, etc. It is more than a pipe-line.

The evidence is that its *surface*—its inner intimal lining—is in dynamic equilibrium with the TDM_{basic} of the cells of the body. *Should this equilibrium dissociate*—as we have already suggested— *the mathematic concept of Equation II says that there will be disastrous loss of body weight beginning first in the initiating organ and then spreading incredibly—"metastasizing"—to destroy the entire organism.*

Furthermore it is both artery and lymph channel which "conducts" the "spreading."

From our point of view—in stating that the biomagnetic fields of the cells of the arterial intimal lining are "in harmony with" the cells of all tissues and all organs—there is no other explanation for the curious "stress-points" we see *upstream* to the organ which becomes "shut down" or "dimmed out." Thus the coronary artery of heart-attack. Thus the lenticulo-striate artery of cerebral hemorrhage and hemiplegia. Thus the arteries of senile dementia. *And, though it may not be at all visible or discernible, the evidence suggests that this is the origin of psychosis—of hallucinosis and delusion.*

It would be simple if we could construct a science-fiction "wall-closet" analogy and say that beneath the arterial intima there may be manufactured or stored hallucinogens, carcinogens, "thrombogens." At night when the mosaic of the arterial intimal lining "separate," these "creatures" ordinarily are destroyed. But in each of the "disaster-diseases," they would emerge—so a fantasy could be constructed—to wreak havoc—unneutralized havoc.

But there is no such "wall-closet" so far as anyone knows. *There is something else.*

The disease of familial xanthomatosis—*the growth of tumors springing from the arterial lining*—capable of killing a child of 10 and her father of 40 at the same time—of the same coronary obstruction due to the same kind of tumor—this disease tells us that the cells of the arterial mosaic are not just inert "material for pipelines"—but rather active dynamic cells—as capable of *net malignancy* as any other tissue of the body. Here the matter is genetic. *Something that should be restraining abnormal growth is missing . . .* What is the stimulus to this growth that most of us can neutralize and keep the walls of our arteries smooth and unobstructed?

The answer (for which mathematic evidence will be given here) demanded by the bioplasma concept is that *all the biomagnetic fields of all tissues are "ordered," not only in relation to themselves and their own cells but in relation to each other and in relation to the "controlling center" of brain-heart dynamics and its monitors*—the psychic representation of which we have already mentioned briefly as the "paraconscious" dream-tension discharging apparatus of the "body-mind."

How does the brain-nerve and heart-artery exercise such order and such control—both over itself and over the body which must be kept intact for brain-heart pulsing and sentience to "sit upon the throne" of the body-mind?

Equation IV (B)—and a final Equation VIII to be presented at the end of Vol. I indicates that the mass of the TDM_{basic} and the mass (and probably the surface) of the heart-artery (and lymphatics) are "tooled" by unsuspected and as yet undiscovered hormone-enzyme factors to "signal" to each other in a very special and subtle way.

Our first task was then to study the obvious aspects of the weight of the heart-artery system and the TDM_{basic}. The circulation-mass would be the mass of the heart plus the mass of the circulating arteries-veins-lymphatics plus the limiting "growth resistance" (magnetic mirror effect) which we know confines—in basic plasma physics—the essential plasma.

Equation IV (B) states then:

$$TDM_{gms.-basic} = Heart_{gms.} + 2(L)_{cms.=gm} + W(t[G.F.f.+ K(FIELD I)*_{birth-4\,yrs.}-0.1t])$$

Here for the first time we introduce the concept of two different biomagnetic fields controlled by brain-heart "center." The first field or FIELD I extending up to 6 years of age is that of the establishment of firm gender organization (*precisely as Freud, one of the most careful observers in the psychology and neurology of children, affirmed*). FIELD II is the period (cf. Figure 5) when the elongating and gender-shaping of the body takes place from 6 years through 18 years and onward, under the impact of the reversal of adrenal percentage growth from negative to positive together with the now rapid efflorescence of the gonad—as the pineal has ceased entirely to grow. (The pineal functions to establish the size of the genitals in relation to the other later hormonal impacts.)

As Table IV (B) shows, the two constants are as follows:
FIELD I (Birth through 4 to 6 years) = 0.6296699 ± 0.1248703 (bearing a certain relationship to 0.2π or 0.62832 which can not be discussed here.)

FIELD II (6 years through 18 years) = 0.245978 ± 0.197402.

We shall see this division of the growth span of all living things— here of man—in other aspects of this work: in the growth of brain and in Equation VII presenting our solution to the "mystery" of heat-production and our view of the meaning of low temperature range in cancer as compared with normal tissue. In Equation IV (B) the length and pelvic width data are those of the Geigy Documenta already used as the empiric basis of body weight. The results show a degree of error so small and in a relationship to the constant close to 0.2π that it is clear that pelvic width as used here is as close as it is possible to get to the "radius" that would be associated in 0.2π.

But here is the mathematic basis for our concept that there is a very fundamental equivalence between the TDM_{basic} —the basic "template" created in and by the bioplasma—and the heart-artery system.

Equation IV (C). TDM_{basic} and the Heart: Gender-Genital Tissue Relationship.

It is our concept that in the bioplasma created at the moment of fertilization there is initiated at once—together with primordial

*K (FIELD II)$_{6\,yrs.-18\,yrs.}$ must be substituted for K(FIELD I) after 4 yrs.

TABLE IV (B)

Age years.	Heart gms.	+	Body Length cms=gms	=	Sum gms.	Pelvic Width cms=gms	[t(G.f.f. + K(FIELD I)−0.1t) **(K(FIELD II) 6-18 years,)]	x		=		TDM (calc) gms	TDM (theor) gms
Birth	24.31	+	100.8	=	125.11	7.9		x	(2.2388607)	=	17.686999	142.80	142.30
½	34.13	+	125.90	=	160.03	11.4		x	(2.4914027)	=	28.526557	188.56	189.60
1	44.00	+	149.4	=	193.4	12.6		x	(2.3053959)	=	29.047988	222.45	224.20
2	58.05	+	174.1	=	232.15	14.25		x	(2.4765467)	=	35.29078	267.44	267.82
3	66.15	+	191.9	=	258.05	15.6		x	(1.0933022)	=	17.055514	275.11	272.00
4	79.46	+	206.6	=	286.06	16.7		x	(0.8043913)	=	13.43334	299.49	297.46
FIELD CHANGE-OVER: from $K_I = 0.6296699 \pm 0.1248703$ to $K_{II} = 0.245978 \pm 0.197402$*													
6	104.76	+	233.4	=	338.16	18.9	t(0.2262378)	x	(29.024386)	=	29.024386	367.18	365.77
8	133.54	+	258.00	=	391.54	20.6	t(0.2657182)	x	(48.005181)	=	48.005181	439.55	441.00
10	158.66	+	278.9	=	437.56	22.1	t(0.2694982)	x	(64.145152)	=	64.145152	501.71	498.40
12	175.02	+	297.7	=	472.72	24.2	t(0.2657182)	x	(82.1159.57)	=	82.1159.57	554.84	556.50
15	249.39	+	328.9	=	578.29	27.1	t(0.2262378)	x	(96.686569)	=	96.686569	684.98	681.76
18	273.42	+	337.0	=	610.42	28.2	t(0.2262378)	x	(119.75083)	=	119.75083	730.17	727.59

** The Field Change-over is dramatized by the insertion of constants of Field I and Field II.

*** After 4 years of age, the factor multiplied by Pelvic Width is merely the time (with Birth as 0.77 years) x the Field$_{II}$ constant. The factor from Birth through 4 years has the more extensive formulation as indicated in the heading.

The relationship between the two constants is interesting but a full discussion must be left for a later report.

provision for brain-heart control with its pulsing and sentience—a *division* between that part of the synthesis that will go to *soma* (body) which is to be precisely "tooled" to the brain-heart necessities— between that and the part of the synthesis that will go to reproduction of the species—i.e. to gender-genital tissue.

If that is true and if the "basic template" is tooled to the heart by the paramagnetic frequency undergoing "step-down" to the pulse at any time then there ought to be another way to determine the TDM_{basic} in relation to FIELD I and to FIELD II, the latter showing the influence of *elongation and gender-shaping*.

We found this to be startlingly true. Thus:

$$TDM_{basic\text{-}gms.} = 2.8026 \, (Heart_{gms.} - G.G. \, Tissue)_{gms.} \times Pulse/sec. \, *$$

in which G.G. designates Gender-Genital Tissue.

Table IV (C) and Figure IV (C) indicate the results in which the curve of gender-genital tissue includes also the empiric data on fluctuations in sexual adipose tissue. This is compared with the empiric data from the Geigy Documenta on the weights of the adrenal-gonadal-reproductive tissue. To my knowledge this is the first such determination in history.

Most striking is the "fit" of the results to each other—tending to confirm the paramagnetic nature of the bioplasma (2.8026) and the resultant TDM_{basic}. ("All the pieces of truth in the world fit together," it is said.)

Equation V. The Equation of the Gender Force factor (G.F.f.)

We have already anticipated and stated this equation above. It represents an entirely original discovery by substituting for the Catecholamine Ratio x 0.040188 the basic "oscillations" of the bioplasma—namely pulse/sec., alpha frequency/sec., and the hitherto unknown G.F.f.

To state it again:

$$(\text{alpha frequency/sec}) \, \left(0.040188 \, \frac{HVA}{(M+NM) \, gms.}\right) - Pulse/sec = G.F.f.$$

Table V shows the results: the G.F.f., the increments in the G.F.f., and the percentage incremental increase which is charted in Figure V. In this latter column it becomes clear why FIELD I—during which myelinization is completed and gender-identity established— comes to its limiting end at 4-6 years of age when its "percentage"

*2.8026 and pulse/sec here are taken as sheer numerical values.

TABLE IV (C)

AGE (Years)	2.8026 x HEART (Grams)	2.8026 x G-G TISSUE (Grams)	PULSE/SEC		TDM (Grams)
Birth	(2.8026 x 24.31) 68.131206 –	(2.8026 x 6.921547) 19.398328 = 48.732878	x 2.92	=	142.30
½	(2.8026 x 34.13) 95.652738 –	(2.8026 x 11.05454) 30.981456 = 64.671282	x 2.89	=	186.90
1	(2.8026 x 44.00) 123.314400 –	(2.8026 x 13.58281) 38.067185 = 85.24722	x 2.63		224.20
2	(2.8026 x 58.05) 162.69093 –	(2.8026 x 11.66104) 32.681216 = 130.00972	x 2.06	=	267.82
3	(2.8026 x 66.15) 185.39199 –	(2.8026 x 12.52970) 35.115745 = 150.27605	x 1.81	=	271.999
4	(2.8026 x 79.46) 222.69459 –	(2.8026 x 15.13448) 42.415753 = 180.27884	x 1.65	=	297.46
6	(2.8026 x 104.76) 293.60037 –	(2.8026 x 16.57692) 46.458478 = 247.1419	x 1.48	=	365.77
8	(2.8026 x 133.54) 374.2592 –	(2.8026 x 17.83849) 49.994177 = 324.26503	x 1.36	=	441.00
10	(2.8026 x 158.66) 444.66051 –	(2.8026 x 22.90819) 64.202496 = 380.45802	x 1.31	=	498.40
12	(2.8026 x 175.02) 490.51105 –	(2.8026 x 18.66912) 52.32207 = 438.18898	x 1.27	=	556.50
15	(2.8026 x 249.39) 698.94041 –	(2.8026 x 57.84683) 162.12151 = 536.8189	x 1.27	=	681.76
18	(2.8026 x 273.42) 766.28689 –	(2.8026 x 67.378666) 188.83543 = 577.45149	x 1.26	=	727.59

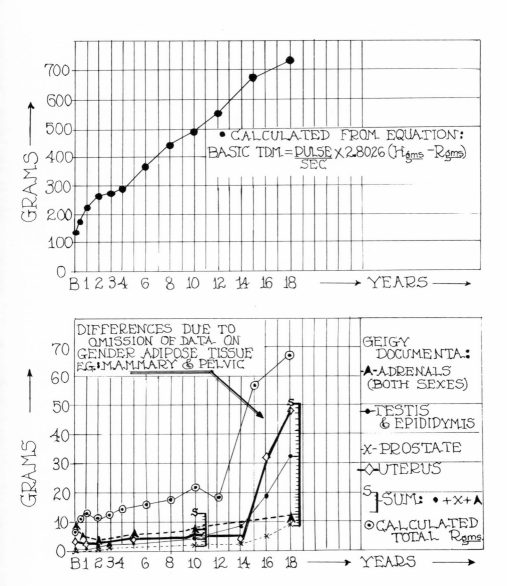

FIG. 4-C: BASIC & REPRODUCTIVE TDM

AUXILIARY TABLE IV (C)

TABLE FOR GENITAL-GENDER GROWTH (Fig. 4-C)

Empiric Genital-Gender Growth (Including Adrenals) gms.

Age (years)	Adrenals (Both Sexes)	Testes & Epidym.	Seminal Vesicles	Prostate	Ovaries	Uterus	Tubes	Empiric Sum (Both Sexes) Average x Pulse	Calculated Average
Birth	9.04*	0.91	0.05	0.82	0.33	3.90*	0.29	15.34 (with adren.) / 6.30 (without ") / av. 3.15 x 2.92 = 9.20	6.9215
½	4.73*	1.33	0.052	0.90	0.62	1.42*	0.26	9.302 / av. 4.65 x 2.89 = 13.44	11.0545
1	4.73	1.82	0.12	1.2	0.62	1.50	0.29	10.28 / av. 5.14 x 2.63 = 13.52	13.5828
2-5	3.56	1.76	0.12	1.1	0.84	2.30	0.29	9.97 / av. 4.99 x 2.06 = 10.27	11.661 (2y) / 12.529 (3y)
5-10	5.19*	2.24	0.099	1.3	1.90	2.80	0.29	13.82 / av. 6.91 x 1.81 = 12.51	15.134 (4y) / 16.576 (6y) / 17.838 (8y)
10-12	7.00	4.00	1.20	1.9	1.90	4.30	0.49	22.19 / av.11.1 x 1.63 = 18.10	22.908 (10y) / 18.669 (12y)
12-14	10.00	8.15	1.20	3.3	3.3	4.30	0.49	30.74 / av.15.37 x 1.48 = 22.79	. . . .
16-18	10.00*	32.00	. . . .	3.8	6.03	32.50	1.05	90.38 / av.45.2 x 1.27 = 57.40	57.847 (15y)
18-30	10.00*	34.66	. . . .	16.6	10.71	49.50	2.13	123.60 / av. 61.8 x 1.26 = 77.87	67.379 (18y)

*The adrenal data at birth are subject to considerable variation and uncertainty due to swelling and hyperplasia of the adrenal cortical tissue . . . . However all studies agree that it shrinks after birth until 2-5 years of age.

**For empiric data on genital-gender reproductive tissue growth of Geigy Documenta Scientific Tables, 1977 and Edith Boyd, Introduction to (motional) increase changes sharply from the negative direction to the positive coinciding with the onset of the bulk of schizophrenic age-incidence curves. Placed in the table is also the pulse frequency/sec and the alpha frequency/sec the latter showing that 12 years of age is the limiting value for any further change in the biomagnetic frequency called "the brain-wave."

It is important at this point in view of the curve of Figure 5 to recall the case referred to by Ketchum[8] in which an incurable cancer underwent a remission as a psychosis appeared; then as the psychosis lessened the cancer reappeared once more. We have seen in Equation II how devastating the "loss of weight" can be when the bioplasma of the body can not support an oscillation frequency of more than 6000/sec instead of the normal 10,000. Here, in Table V, we can see the link between the "weight" function of the percentage growth in G.F.f. important to schizophrenia and the loss of body weight should the G.F.f. diminish sharply.

Here a new concept begins to take place—that precisely as Freud suspected and as all analysis shows—*there exists in every cell in the body*—to us, in the bioplasma—*a critical sexual force represented by the G.F.f. oscillation, loss of which can mean a disaster to body (cancer) and loss of which to brain can mean a reciprocal disaster (schizophrenia).*

This was in Freud's terms of course "the libido." He could in no way have made it measurable or quantitatively seen—and yet, as always—his accuracy of observation and his future vision are incredibly powerful.

* * * * * * * *

Equation VI.

To this equation and to Table VI and Figure 6, we have already made reference as the application of Equation II to various species *when the basis of our orientation is the bioplasma and the frequencies which it can support and propagate.*

For the first time in medical history, I believe, there is presented here the body, brain, heart, as *oscillatory mass forces organized around the species-pulse* as "ordinate," and its range as "abscissa." It is clear that the dolphin is closest to man—of the species presented.

I believe that making the bioplasma oscillating mass-forces the basis for this view enables us for the first time to bring order to chaos.

The question already discussed: "Why does a mouse live only 400-600 days when a elephant can live as long as 50 years or more?" we have tried to show is in reality an irrelevant question. The question is—in

TABLE V

Age years	Pulse per sec.	alpha freq. per sec.	Gender Force factor (G.F.f.)	Increment per year in G.F.f.	Percentage Increase in G.F.f.	Catecholamine Ratio per gram/year (x 0.040188)
Birth	2.92	1.85	-2.2302385	————	————	0.37284
½	2.89	5.10	-1.334194	0.8960445	-0.8035419	0.30506
1	2.63	6.55	-0.974684	0.359510	-0.5390	0.25272
2	2.06	7.70	-0.416512	0.558172	-0.5727	0.21344
3	1.81	8.30	-0.182201	0.254311	-0.6106	0.19853
4 5*	1.65	8.30	-0.1408359 -0.0559162	0.0213659 0.0849192	-0.1317199 -0.6026655	0.181827
6 7*	1.48	9.10	+0.0283314 -0.066044	0.003152 0.037037	-1.5186868 +1.2770	0.165256
8 9*	1.36	9.20	+0.103076	0.037037 0.015202	+0.5608 +0.1475	0.15903
10 11*	1.31	9.20	+0.133480 +0.193730	0.015202 0.060250	+0.1285 +0.4514	0.15690
12 13* 14*	1.27	9.20	+0.253980 +0.275970 +0.297969	0.060250 0.021999 0.021999	+0.3110 +0.0866 +0.0797	0.16565
15 16* 17*	1.27	10.20	+0.319976 +0.362341 +0.404706	0.021999 0.042365 0.042365	+0.0738 +0.1324 +0.1168	0.155889
18	1.26	10.20	+0.447072	0.042365	+0.1047	0.16737

*The values for these years have been approximated. Later studies to refine the values for these intervals must wait upon more adequate catecholamine data for each year.

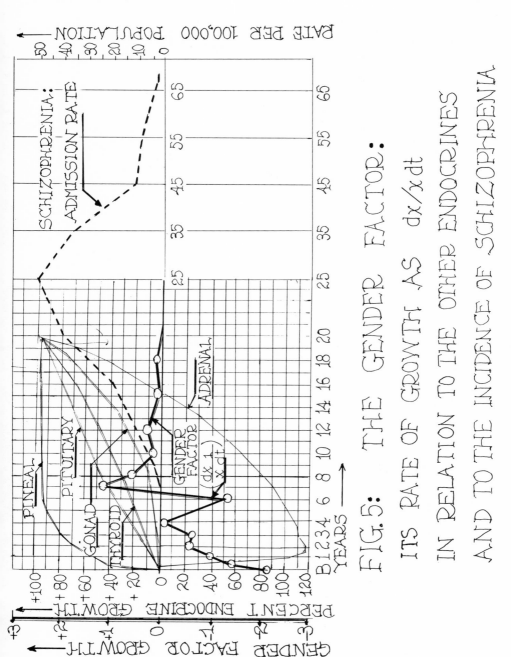

FIG. 5:   THE GENDER FACTOR:

ITS RATE OF GROWTH AS   dx/xdt

IN RELATION TO THE OTHER ENDOCRINES

AND TO THE INCIDENCE OF SCHIZOPHRENIA

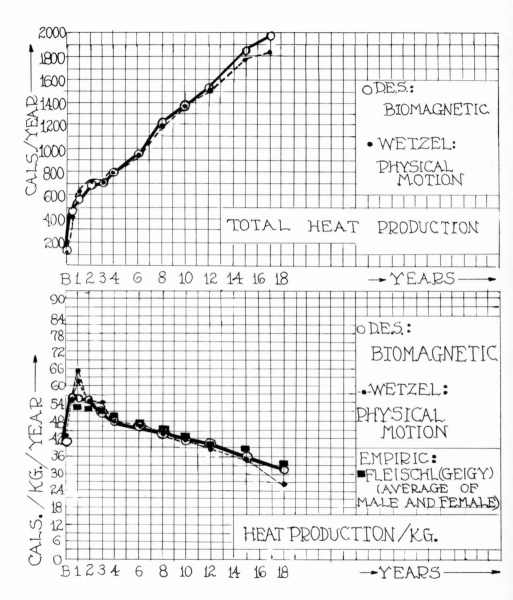

FIG.5-A: BIOMAGNETIC HEAT PRODUCTION*

*Values shown in auxiliary Table VIIA, pg. 74. This graph anticipates but is placed here to illustrate the Gender Force factor of figure 5 in its "energizing role." It solves the long standing "mystery" of the head and shoulders configuration of basal metabolism from birth to six years of age corresponding to the "climb" of the Gender Force factor during these early years.

relation to our brain-heart adaptative characteristics and power—*how many heart-beats do we live?*

Figure VI illustrates that while all living things have a commensurate "heart-beat life-span," their brain-heart power and their evolving for aquatic or terrestrial life is the issue, once one estimates and thinks in terms of heart-beat number. Thus we can see why the shark is no match for the dolphin—the shark being merely an "eating machine" while the dolphin has been called "the man of the sea." Our equations based on our concept of the bioplasma thus embrace and bring into order more phenomena than have ever been organized under one aegis—under one concept:—that of life-process as life-process growth pulsing, sentient, and genderizing in the evolutionary "miracle" of the bioplasma. Here begins the science of longevity.

Equation VI reports only the adult of each species and it may be written:

Adult Species

$$\text{Mass}_{gms.} = \frac{[4.18879 \ r^3] \ [\text{Species Pulse} \times 10^X] \ [\text{Brain}_{gms.}^{adult} / \text{Heart}_{gms.}^{adult}]}{2.8026 \times 10^6 \ \text{cycles/sec/gauss}}$$

Three major points are established in Figure 6 for each species at its "pulse ordinate" along the "pulse-rate range abscissa" using the actual ordinates of body mass in relation to pulse-ordinate, of body-heart cyclic ratio in relation to pulse-ordinate and brain-heart ratio in relation to pulse-ordinate. The first point then in mass-dimensional, the second is bioplasma activity index, the third is brain-heart power adaptation.

In a later study we hope to return to details of *the evolutionary aspects of bioplasma organization in the various species.*

* * * * * * * *

Equation VII. Biomagnetic Heat-Production.

It is on the basis for this equation that we shall return now to further consideration of the importance of TDM*basic* equivalence to heart-artery mass. It will appear as the corresponding Table VII indicates in what we have called "The Systems Distribution Divisor" or, more simply, the S.D.D.

Here again—and exquisitely—we shall see the operation of the two major biomagnetic fields of growth (FIELD I and FIELD II) the

TABLE VI

	Man	Dolphin (Tursiops)	Baboon	Mouse (Albino)	Elephant	Horse (Grade)	Whale (Large)	Whale (Small White)	Whale (Small White)	Whale (Beluga)	Tiger Shark
BODY gms.	59,820 (61,556)	142,430	19,500	20	6,654,000	521,640	21,708,000	303,230	441,310	1,363,630	200,000
BRAIN gms.	1345.24	1735	175	0.3	5712	655	33,739	2354	2349	7425.54	107.5
HEART gms.	273.42	738	79.94	0.18	26080	3260	116,000	1722	2454	6409.06	291.5
BRAIN/HEART RATIO	4.92	2.35	2.1891	1.7	0.2190	0.2009	0.2908	1.36	0.9572	1.1586	0.3869
LENGTH	173.1 (174.6)	259.08	120	8	686	273.4	1343	370	400	495	736.26
½ LENGTH cms.	86.5 (87.3)	129.54	60	4	343	136.7	671.83	185	200	247.5	368.13
BODY EPR cycles/sec/gauss	1.26×10^4 (12,600)	1.87×10^4 (18,700)	2.75×10^4 (27,500)	12.0×10^4 (120,000)	0.5×10^6 (500,000)	0.68×10^6 (680,000)	0.167×10^6 (167,000)	0.24×10^5 (24,000)	0.40×10^5 (40,000)	0.5194×10^5 (51,940)	0.725×10^4 (7250)
HEART EPR cycles/sec/gauss	1.26	1.87	2.75	12.0	0.5	0.68	1.67	0.24	0.40	0.5194	0.725
PULSE/MIN.	75.6	112.2	165	720	30	43.5	10	14.4	24	31.2	43.5
(EMPIRIC)	76	84-140	120-190	660-800	25-55	32-48	10	12-18	18-32	24-36	39-48
BODY gms. (Calc.)	59,967 (61,647)	142,774	19,435	19.514	6,634,413	521,633	22,009,819	308,882	457,805	1,363,605	209,154

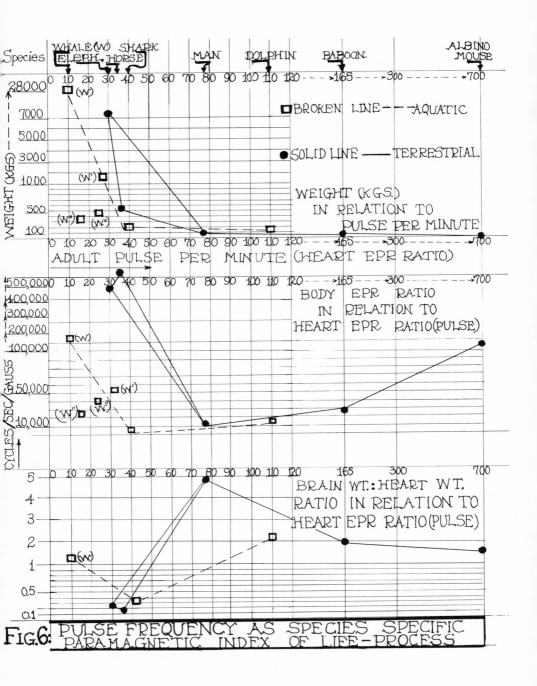

FIG.6: PULSE FREQUENCY AS SPECIES SPECIFIC PARAMAGNETIC INDEX OF LIFE-PROCESS

latter appearing at 4-6 years of age after myelinization and the negative phase of the G.F.f. have been completed.

Using Table VII to enlarge upon our simple "listing" of the equation, we write:

$$\text{Total Heat}_{calories} = \text{TDM}_{gms.\text{basic}} \left[\frac{\text{FIELD}^2}{\text{I}\rightarrow\text{II}} \left(\frac{84.784758}{4.1840 \times \text{S.D.D.}} \right) + \frac{2.00229\,\text{G.F.f.}}{\text{alpha freq. } + t} \right]$$

Table VII describes the quantities used as follows:

Column (1): TDM_{basic} for each year as indicated in the *Age* column.

Column (2): shows the brain-gender variables that will be part of the S.D.D. The brain-gender variables include the *constant K = 1.000000* to express the TDM_{basic}: Heart-Artery equivalence already mentioned above; (B) the rate x 10-3 of the growth of the brain; and (G) the quantity x 10-2 of the gender-genital mass each year. *It is this column to which we shall refer in illustrating the disastrous results of the cancer process when TDM_{basic} and Heart-Artery equivalence is shattered.*

Column (3): is the square root of Column (2).

Column (4): is the G.F.f. x 10-2 at birth. After birth: 0.01 (G.F.F.-Increment in G.F.f.).

Column (5): is the post-natal time-variable of 0.012 t with Birth as zero t.

The Systems Distribution Divisor (S.D.D.) is the *sum* of Columns (3), (4), and (5), multiplied by 2π x 4.1840, the joules-to-calories converter.

Column (6): is the relationship of G.F.f. as expressive of its biomagnetic field (and hence it is multiplied by *g* the gyromagnetic constant = 2.00229) in relation to the alpha frequency + time (beginning with birth as 0.77 years.)*

We have now briefly listed all the variables in Equation VII except that which we have called FIELD I → II—the numerical value of which is squared since these fields are conceived of as operating symmetrically.

The inclusion of the value of the field completes the equation and this is indicated in:

Column (7): Total Heat, in calories. (I) indicates results of Table 7 A.

Column (8): is Body Weight in kilograms and

Column (9): shows Heat/kilo in calories/kilo. In this Column the

*Data in Table V.

additional result marked (I) is the result given in the simplified Table VII (A) where the complexity of Columns (3), (4), and (5) is reduced to a constant except for the ages 6 months, 15 years and 18 years. The results of Table VII (A) compare with Wetzel's 1937 results noted in *Column (10)* as (B) while his first series (Series XIX) is indicated by (A) more in conformity with our full and complex equation VII.

We must now pay some attention to the field variables.

It will be observed in Table VII that between 3 and 4 years of age—at the end of the myelinization period, we have indicated the "Field Changeover" in our biomagnetic concept as compared with the very brilliant Wetzel solution *based on Newtonian analogy 44 years ago* in 1932.

The brilliance and accuracy of Wetzel's work—leading to the famous Wetzel Grid—is unquestionable.

But our goal was different. It was based—from the very beginning (*The Growth Concept of Nervous Integration* in 1949)—upon the brain as a biomagnetic force of growth—instead of on the sheer numbers of dead weight. From the very beginning our interest was in life-process growth pulsing, sentient, and genderizing, gradually evolving the concept of the bioplasma presented here.

The two fields—FIELD I and FIELD II—have the following values based upon the value of the Bohr magneton or $(0.92732)^2 = 0.8599223$ for FIELD II because in FIELD II, the value of H (or Field Strength) is unity or 1. And the value 0.8599223 holds from 4 years to 18 years. Therefore, *after* 3 years of age, as Table VII shows, the S.D.D. is divided into 2.7733487. *Before* that—under the aegis of FIELD I from birth to 4 years of age when the nervous system is myelinizing and gender-force is firmly establishing the basis for gender-shaping and size (and for gender-identity) the S.D.D. is divided into 3.225115 because the value of FIELD I is $(1)^2 = 1$ due to the greater value of H_{gauss} in biomagnetic field-strength. Here in FIELD I, the value of H_{gauss} is of course—because the entire energy of the EPR level-difference is given as $g\mu_o H$—1.0783763. Squared— this amounts to 1.1628954—a very critically greater field-strength than that of FIELD II.

Table VII (B) illustrates the effect of the "change-over" upon the ensuing values.

* * * * * * * *

Consequences of the Pathologic Alteration of the TDM_basic-Heart-Artery equivalence constant of 1.000000 in Column (2) in Table VII.
We must here interrupt our "listing"—Equation VIII is the final

major equation presented in Part I—to examine the consequences if:

(1) K in Column (2) is doubled,—because the heart-artery surface (and mass) has become acutely reduced in its relationship to the "basic template" of the bioplasma—the total heat at 18 years of age will be reduced to 1252.5345 calories instead of 1582.1808 and the unit heat/kilo will be, if weight has not yet fallen, *20.347886!* . . . This is at least 5 calories beneath the maintenance value of 25.70 reached by 18 years of age. . . . *The more severe the increase in K due to diminution in the heart-artery integration with the basic "template" TDM, the more the total and unit heat will fall.* Unless weight falls with it, life-process growth maintenance for tissue-repair will fail . . . *Or, the "center-control" may deflect the threat by increasing blood-pressure*—which is this writer's explanation for so-called "genetic hypertension"—a failure of integration as described, with all the consequences of stress at the artery *just before the capillary bridge* as we have already noted—because it is here that "Horatio"—the increment of peripheral resistance, must make its stand . . . Here begins the process that leads to heart-attack and stroke:

(2) the bioplasma of the cell responds by a lower "resting potential"—*the condition for re-instating growth as energy in motion.* The result is neoplasm—on the arteries' intimal lining as in the tumors—the deadly tumors of familial xanthomatosis, or in the organ tissue-cells supplied *as cancer* because the lower "resting potential" will *invite* previously neutralized toxins,—tar-nicotine, asbestos, etc.

(3) and, a similar process in the cerebral cortical arteries—*because of the failure of the genderizing-sexual force*—as illustrated in Figure 5—will interfere with the imagery-components of the visual and auditory system and produce hallucinations and delusions at precisely the point when the "motion" of the genderizing-sexual force changes from negative to positive, in the genesis of schizophrenia. The same forces are undoubtedly involved in homosexuality in gender-identity confusion, and in that clowning tragic delusion—beginning early in infancy—of the male "trans-sexual" who amputates his male genitals, has an artificial vagina made by surgery, injects himself with hormone and silicon—*and plays tennis and football like a man.*

* * * * * * * *

Equation VIII. The Equation of Bioplasma Body-Synthesis

Leaving various considerations for a special section in the *Appendix* to this "listing" of equations, we must here state that, if the concept of the bioplasma is valid, then the synthesis of body mass must depend upon a very specific "partitioning proportion" in every cell of

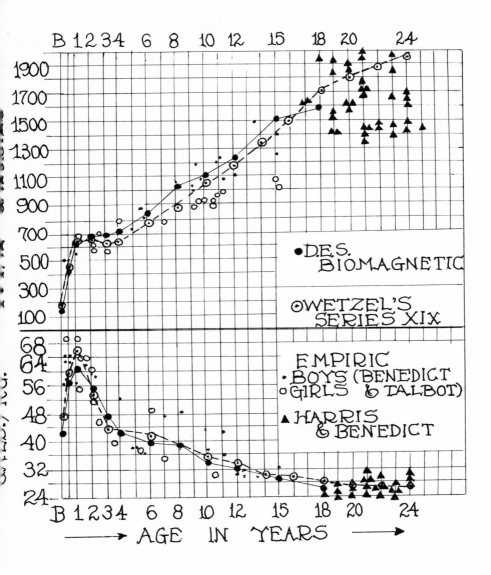

FIG. 7: HEAT PRODUCTION WITH BIOMAGNETIC FACTOR

TABLE VII
COMPONENTS OF THE EQUATION (7) FOR
BIOMAGNETIC CONCEPT OF HEAT-PRODUCTION – THE FULL EQUATION.

	(1)	(2)	(3) + (4) + (5)			(6)
AGE (yrs.)	TDM (gms.)	Brain-Gender Variables	Square Root of (2)	Combined G.F. Factors	+ 0.012(t) (post-natal)	g (G.F.) / Alpha F.+t
B	142.30	1.000000 (K) 0.375953 (B) 0.069215 (G) 1.445168	1.2021514 − 0.02230285 ——— TOTAL OF COLUMNS 3, 4, and 5. 1.1798812 (divided into 3.225115=2.7334235+(6)=*1.0290			−1.7044214
½	186.90	1.000000 (K) 0.34657 (B) 0.110545 (G) 1.457115	1.2071101 −0.04381485 + 0.006 TOTAL OF COLUMNS 3, 4, and 5. 1.1692953 (divided into 3.225115=2.7581698+(6)=*2.338791			−0.4193784
1	224.20	1.000000 (K) 0.17817 (B) 0.13583 (G) 1.314000	1.1462983 −0.0615174 + 0.006 TOTAL OF COLUMNS 3, 4, and 5. 1.0907809 (divided into 3.225115=2.9567028+(6)=*2.779609			−0.1770938
2	267.82	1.000000 (K) 0.10255 (B) 0.11661 (G) 1.21916	1.104155 +0.014166 + 0.024 TOTAL OF COLUMNS 3, 4, and 5. 1.207217 (divided into 3.225115=2.6715288+(6)=*2.591875			−0.079654
3	272.00	1.000000 (K) 0.11292 (B) 0.12529 (G) 1.23821	1.1127488 +0.00921 + 0.036 TOTAL OF COLUMNS 3, 4, and 5. 1.1579588			−0.0269156
	BIOMAGNETIC FIELD REDUCTION:		**(divided into 3.225115=2.7851724+(6)=*2.758257 **(divided into 2.7733487=2.3950322+(6)=*2.368117			
		FIELD CHANGE-OVER			AVERAGE=*2.563187	
4	297.46	1.000000 (K) 0.03875 (B) 0.15134 (G) 1.19009	1.0909124 −0.011947 + 0.048 TOTAL OF COLUMNS 3, 4, and 5. 1.1269654 (divided into 2.7733487=2.4608995+(6)=*2.439324			−0.0215756
6	365.77	1.000000 (K) 0.08620 (B) 0.16576 (G) 1.25196	1.1188101 −0.0032155 + 0.072 TOTAL OF COLUMNS 3, 4, and 5. 1.1940256 (divided into 2.7733487=2.3226878+(6)=*2.326347			+0.0036592
8	441.00	1.000000 (K) 0.019990 (B) 0.17838 (G) 1.19837	1.0947008 +0.0140013 + 0.096 TOTAL OF COLUMNS 3, 4, and 5. 1.2047121 (divided into 2.7733487=2.3020842+(6)=*2.313569			+0.0114851
10	498.40	1.000000 (K) 0.04561 (B) 0.22908 (G) 1.27469	1.1290217 +0.0148682 + 0.120 TOTAL OF COLUMNS 3, 4, and 5. 1.2638899 (divided into 2.7733487=2.1942961+(6)=*2.207679			+0.133833
12	556.50	1.000000 (K) 0.03437 (B) 0.18669 (G) 1.22106	1.1050158 (at limit=0) + 0.144 TOTAL OF COLUMNS 3, 4, and 5. 1.2490158 (divided into 2.7733487=2.2204272+(6)=*2.243574			+0.023147
15	681.76 (at lim.)	1.000000 (K) 0.000000 (B) 0.57847 (G) 1.57847	1.2563717 ——— (at lim.=0) TOTAL OF COLUMNS 3, 4, and 5. 1.2563717 (divided into 2.7733487=2.2074269+(6)=*2.23209			+0.0246701
18	727.59	1.000000 (K) 0.000000 (B) 0.67379 (G) 1.67379	1.2937503 ——— ——— TOTAL OF COLUMNS 3, 4, and 5. 1.2937503 (divided into 2.7733487=2.1436506+(6)=*2.17455			+0.0308998

*The final resultant to be multiplied by TDM.

The product is illustrated in Column 7 as "TOTAL HEAT."

CONTRAST BETWEEN THE NEWTONIAN CONCEPT (WETZEL) AND THE BIOMAGNETIC CONCEPT (D.E.S.)

(7)	(8)	(9)	(10)		
Total Heat (cals.)	Body Wt. (kgs.)	Heat per kg.	Wetzel's Data (1932 as A and 1937 as B) Total Heat (cals.)	Body Wt. (kgs.)	Heat/kg.
146.4267	3.44	42.57	155.13 (A)	3.251	47.72
(141.41) (I)		(41.12)(I)	140.61 (B)	3.25	43.25
437.1200	7.56	57.82	446.97 (A)	7.565	59.08
(425.91) (I)		(56.34) (I)	419.74 (B)	7.57	55.48
623.1884	10.06	61.95	664.09 (A)	10.062	66.00
(616.01) (I)		(61.23) (I)	616.01 (B)	10.06	61.22
694.1559	12.48	55.62	680.89 (A)	12.695	53.63
(701.29) (I)		(56.19) (I)	780.24 (B)	12.70	55.79
Average of: 750.2459 & 644.1272	14.711		607.41 (A)	14.192	42.80
697.1869		47.39	722.97 (B)	15.04	48.07
(726.58) (I)		(49.34) (I)			
BIOMAGNETIC CONCEPT			**NEWTONIAN CONCEPT**		
725.6013	16.74	43.35	633.93 (A)	15.486	40.94
(796.18) (I)		(47.56) (I)	801.24 (B)	16.70	47.95
850.9079	21.556	39.47	760.63 (A)	18.852	40.35
(988.25) (I)		(45.85) (I)	978.12 (B)	20.45	47.83
1020.284	26.867	37.98	897.39 (A)	23.759	37.77
(1194.96) (I)		(44.48) (I)	1199.53 (B)	26.34	45.54
1100.3072	32.63	33.72	1041.81 (A)	29.967	34.76
(1351.44) (I)		(41.42) (I)	1371.71 (B)	32.53	42.17
1248.5489	38.996	32.02	1193.49 (A)	36.917	32.33
(1514.41) (I)		(38.84) (I)	1510.67 (B)	38.68	39.06
1521.7496	52.30	29.09	1343.74 (A)(14	44.000	30.54
			1792.78 (B) yr)	48.02	36.87
(1793.58) (I)		(34.29) (I)	1481.77 (A)(16	50.712	29.22
			1794.38 (B) yr)	56.00	32.04
1582.1808	61.556	25.70	1602.00 (A)	56.709	28.25
(1838.47) (I)		(29.87) (I)	1838.47 (B)	63.00	29.18

TABLE VII (A)

AUXILIARY TABLE FOR HEAT PRODUCTION (Equation VII – Simplified) (Noted as I)

AGE (yrs.)	$\dfrac{84.784758}{*K(1.1952981)}$	$\dfrac{2.0029(G.F.)}{\text{alpha fr.}^{+\ +}}$	Total Factor	x	TDM = (gms.)	Total Heat (Cals.)	Body Wt. (kgs.)	Unit Heat (Cals/kg)
Birth	2.6981682	-1.7044214	0.9937468		142.30	141.41	3.44	41.12
½	2.6981682	-0.4193784	2.278789		186.90	425.91	7.56	56.34
1	*(2.9821624)	-0.2345673	2.747595		224.20	616.01	10.06	61.23
2	2.6981682	-0.079654	2.6185142		267.82	701.29	12.48	56.19
3	2.6981682	-0.269156	2.6712526		272.00	726.58	14.711	49.34
4	2.6981682	-0.215756	2.6765926		297.46	796.18	16.74	47.56
6	2.6981682	+0.0036592	2.7018274		365.77	988.25	21.556	45.85
8	2.6981682	+0.0114851	2.7096533		441.00	1194.96	26.867	44.48
10	2.6981682	+0.0133833	2.7115515		498.40	1351.44	32.63	41.42
12	2.6981682	+0.023147	2.7213152		556.50	1514.41	38.996	38.84
15	**(2.6061413)	+0.246701	2.6308114		681.76	1793.58	52.30	34.29
18	**(2.4958953)	+0.0308998	2.5267951		727.59	1838.47	61.556	29.87

*K here may be treated as a practical constant with these exceptions for the following ages: birth, 6 mos., 2, 3, 4, 6, 8, 10, and 12 years – in which it has the value: 1.1952981 . . . .

**These values are different due to the gender changes in length and width consonant with the curves of growth of the adrenal and the gonad. The adrenal diminishes sharply at one year and, together with the gonad, increases sharply at 15 to 18-20 years . . . The diminution of the adrenal (negative adrenal growth) corresponds in time (at 6 mos. to 1 year) to the sharp increase in brain and pineal gland . . . At 1 year, K = 1.0814687; at 15 years, K = 1.2375059; and at 18 years, K = 1.2921677 . . . These values have been calculated on the basis of the length and width data of the Geigy Documenta. (Cf. Fig. 5 A pg. 64, for graph of these values.)

AUXILIARY TABLE VII (B)

TO ILLUSTRATE HOW BIOMAGNETIC HEAT-PRODUCTION
SHOWS THE DIFFERENCES WITH FIELD VALUE OF H = 1.16****
COMPARED WITH FIELD VALUE OF H = 1****

AGE (yrs.)	VALUES WITH FIELD H=1.16 Total Heat in Calories (Calories/Kg.)		VALUES WITH FIELD H=1.00 Total Heat in Calories (Calories/Kg.)
		Fields (Averaged at 3 years)	
Birth	*** 146.42663 *** (42.56588)	(Kgs.=3.44)	196.77521 (26.72711)
½	*** 437.12045 *** (57.820165)	(Kgs.=7.56)	363.63356 (48.09967)
1	*** 610.30218 *** (60.66622)	(Kgs.=10.06)	491.65525 (48.872291)
2	*** 694.15524 *** (55.621413)	(Kgs.=12.48)	593.93185 (47.590693)
3	750.24517 (50.998923)	(Kgs.=14.711	644.12763 (43.78544)

(As myelinization is completed) Average of Both Fields

*** 697.68640 (Kgs.=14.711)
*** (47.42617)

AGE	VALUES WITH FIELD H=1.16		VALUES WITH FIELD H=1.00
4	829.15798 (49.53154)	(Kgs.=16.74)	*** 712.11142 *** (42.539511)
6	986.13551 (45.747611)	(Kgs.=21.556	*** 848.18611 *** (39.348028)
8	1207.4548 (44.932538)	(Kgs.=26.867	*** 1038.8108 *** (38.664934)
10	1278.4548 (39.180349)	(Kgs.=32.63	*** 1100.3071 *** (33.72072)
12	1449.8293 (37.178923)	(Kgs.=38.997)	*** 1248.5450 *** (32.017278)
15	1766.9000 (33.783938)	(Kgs.=52.30	*** 1521.754 *** (29.096634)
18	1836.2485 (29.830536)	(Kgs.=61.556	*** 1582.1832 *** (25.703151)

***These are the composite values charted in Figure 7.

****Divide H by implicit constant 2×10^9. Cf. Footnote page 30.

the body. As a bioplasma dominated by electromagnetic interactions of which the DNA comprises the "magic mountains" in the bioplasma landscape, each cell will have to demonstrate at least *three major sets of components—in order for life-process growth pulsing, sentient, and genderizing to exist and to perpetuate itself and its species.* These three major sets of components, moreover, must satisfy the known major characteristics of a bioplasma—akin to—but not identical with the plasma of modern plasma physics.

These three sets of components satisfying the major attributes of a *bio*-plasma are the following:

(1) A portion of every cell—different in each system—but, in the bulk, definite—will go to the *semi-conductor* nature of the nervous system—a phenomenon which all modern research into brain cells confirms. If we treat this element as obeying the laws of the "coil," (whereby in magnetic coils electric currents are induced—analogically speaking), then because of our mirror-image symmetry, the co-efficient of the nervous "coils" will depend on $(2 \pi r)^2$ or ($\pi^2 =$ 9.8696505) $(4 r^2)$ in which $4(r^2)$ will be expressed by the tissue itself synthesizing along its nervous radius. So too the cord as well as the brain—except that as we have seen the "segmental cord" stands in exponential relationship to the body in the exponent illustrated in Table IV as 0.90015×10^3 with its time increment of 0.08 per year. 0.90015 is the sum of $(0.62832 = 0.2\pi)$ and of $(0.27183 = 0.1\ e)$.

We have found that this first component is satisfied by the formulation for the brain-cord "contribution" made by every cell:

$$\pi^2 \ \text{Brain}_{gms.} + \pi_e^2 \ \text{Cord}_{gms.} \ , \text{or} \ \pi^2 \ (\text{Brain}_{gms.} + e\ \text{Cord}_{gms.})$$

$(\pi^2 = 9.8696505 \text{ and } \pi^2 e = 26.82867.)$

(2) Every cell of the bioplasma must be capable of both *supporting and propagating* specific oscillating forces at a specific frequency. Again, this "contribution" will be different for every system but,—in the bulk—it must relate to the *heart* as the major acoustic oscillating propagating force. This must be done at a consonant rate which adds up to the *pulse of the heart* multiplied—in man—as Equation II as shown—by a factor of 10^4 (—and in other species by a species-specific factor as shown in Equation VI and Figure 6).

In Equation VIII, however, we do not resort to this previous formulation but instead must confirm the synthesizing of body mass by another route. The multiplication of heart as *mass x pulse* (as *frequency*) is a measure of the rate of synthesis. And, to this must be added the countering and gender-shaping length and width forces of the adrenal-pineal-gonadal complex we have already called the "gender-genital mass" and the G.F.f. In addition, the pulse itself must be seen as the expression of its "pacemaker" which, in view of its biomagnetic quality and quantity, must have the constant (g^2) where g

is the gyromagnetic factor already mentioned in "electronic paramagnetic resonance" comments and is equal to 2.00229. ($g^2 =$ 4.0091652).

The second component of our equation then will satisfy bioplasma conditions when expressed as follows:

Heart$_{gms.}$ (Bioplasma Factor A) (Bioplasma Factor B).

Bioplasma Factor B is the one just described and it may be written as:

(4.0091652 + [Gend.-Gen. Weight$_{gms.}$ x (0.040188 Cate. Ratio$_{gms.}$ -0.15588)]

Table VIII supplies all these values of Factor B and also of Factor A now to be discussed but first presented as follows:

$$\left(\frac{TDM_{basic}}{31.490255} + \frac{t}{Shaping\ Ratio^*} \right)$$

In Factor A, the first term: $\dfrac{TDM_{basic}}{31.490255}$ contains in the denominator the *product* of (2.8026 x 10^6 cycles per sec per gauss)^2 or, when the units are cancelled out, the value of = 7.8545667 and $g^2 =$ 4.0091652. We shall detail the reason for this below. The second term: $\dfrac{t}{Shaping\ Ratio}$ will represent the *time-increment* in the synthesis of the "basic template" or TDM_{basic} . But the dimensions of the time increment will depend upon gender-shaping, i.e. the male is taller and less wide in the pelvic radius in relation to shoulder span and the female is shorter and more wide in the pelvic radius in relation to shoulder span. The "Shaping Ratio" is then the expression of male shaping ratio to female shaping ratio. Using the body-length and pelvic width in the empiric Geigy Documenta, we have found that the *Shaping Ratio* (= male shaping ratio / female shaping ratio) is, for all discernible reasons less than *unity or 1*, up to 12 years of age. Then as has been known for centuries, at 12 the female *widens* and the Shaping Ratio becomes 0.644794. But at 15 years-18 years, the male of the human species will elongate at a much greater rate than the female and the Shaping Ratio becomes *0.8775524 at 15 years and 1.3184352 at 18 years*.

* * * * * * * *

*Shaping Ratio is always Gender Shaping Ratio or G.S.R.

We must briefly discuss the first term of Bioplasma Factor A. *First* of all, the mirror-image symmetry of life-process growth will demand that the constant 2.8026 be squared, yielding 7.8545667. *Second*, again, the synthesis of the "basic template" is here conceived as *per* the difference in energy levels resulting from the movement of free electrons toward or away from the magnetic field direction. As we have already seen, this is satisfied by the equation:

Difference in Energy = $h\nu$ = $g\mu_\circ$ *H*, the square of which we have already discussed in Equation VII. Since the synthesis of tissue can only go on—from the point of view of this theory—on the basis of "free" electrons in proportion to *fixed* electrons in the "lattice" of structures, then synthesis of tissue will proceed *per* $g\mu_\circ$ *H*, or per *g*.

Therefore the first term of Bioplasma Factor A can be seen to consist of the following:

$$- \frac{(2.8026 \times 10^6 \text{ cycles/sec/gauss})^2 \times \text{Synthesizing Mass}_{gms.}}{(2.8026 \times 10^6 \text{ cycles/sec/gauss})^2 \times (g^2 = 4.0091652)_{gms.}} = \frac{\text{TDM}_{\text{basic - gms}}}{31.490255_{gms.}}$$

(3) The third component will be, of necessity, π or 3.1416 x its co-efficient since the entire equation again represents the "giant spiral" of the living, pulsing, and sentient life-process growth coming into existence out of the DNA double helical "magic mountains" to make the species-body. When we set up our task with these theoretical orientations, then the co-efficient of π is no less than: (-400) to make the third term of Equation VIII = $-400\,\pi$.

All three terms are set equal to the body weight we have used throughout this work: showing body weight to follow a law as the exponential result of the segmental cord, the exponent being equal to $(0.2\,\pi + 0.1e + .08t) \times 10^3$, showing body weight to follow the law of Equations I and II.

Here is the fourth approach—and indeed all four are needed to satisfy our concept of *proof* in agreement with Einstein's view that:

    . . . pure mathematical construction enables us to discover the concepts and the laws connecting them which give us a key to the understanding of the phenomena of Nature.

Table VIII illustrates Equation VIII which is stated thus:

$$\pi^2 \text{ Brain}_{gms.} + \pi^2 e \text{ Cord}_{gms.} + \text{Heart}_{gms.} \text{ (Factor A)(Factor B)} - 400\pi = \text{Body Wt.}_{gms.}$$

with Factor A and Factor B as already described.

This concludes the presentation of the major equations of the new science of the bioplasma and its concept of life-process as life-process growth pulsing and sentient, except for Equation IX in the Appendix.

AGE years	π^2 Brain gms.	π^2 e Cord gms.	Heart gms.	Factor A	(Heart x A x B) gms.	Factor B	-400π	=	Body Weight gms.
Birth	3745.5329 (379.53)	102.1085 (3.82)	24.31	5.2998334	(848.99867)	6.589612	-1256.64	=	3440
½	7166.3532 (726.10)	214.99452 (8.0432)	34.13	7.4887883	(1435.2922)	5.6155527	-1256.64	=	7560
1	8929.2702 (904.72)	270.89759 (10.1346)	44.00	9.0339585	(2116.4747)	5.3245429	-1256.64	=	10060
2	9941.4028 (1007.27)	308.31527 (11.72313)	58.05	12.833932	(3486.9227)	4.6803723	-1256.64	=	12480
3	11055.883 (1120.19)	343.62985 (12.8556)	66.15	15.199007	(4568.1271)	4.543527	-1256.64	=	14711
4	11435.34 (1158.64)	364.89889 (13.6513)	79.46	15.990468	(6196.3695)	4.8767173	-1256.64	=	16740
6	12288.701 (1245.10)	413.80138 (15.4808)	104.76	21.739561	(10110.138)	4.4392626	-1256.64	=	21556
8	12486.380 (1265.13)	462.5515 (17.3046)	133.54	27.199957	(15174.709)	4.1777343	-1256.64	=	26867
10	12936.249 (1310.71)	508.44152 (19.0214)	158.66	31.568481	(20441.951)	4.0813254	-1256.64	=	32630
12	13275.765 (1345.11)	554.81535 (20.7563)	175.02	37.47692	(26422.06)	4.0282381	-1256.64	=	38996
				Limit of EEG and Growth of the Brain. – Period of Dramatic Increase in Gender-Genital Sexual Growth.**					
15	13278.035 (1345.34)	658.69605 (24.6426)	249.39	39.620308	(39619.908)	4.0097436	-1256.64	=	52300
18	13277.048 (1345.24)	697.59886 (26.0980)	273.42	37.341813 ***	(48837.993)	4.7833499 ***	-1256.64	=	61556

**This hiatus in the table indicates the limit of EEG and Brain Growth. After 12 years of age, as can be seen in the above data, the brain weight is practically at equilibrium at 1345.11 – 1345.24 grams. So too, the limit is marked in the EEG (cf. Table V showing the empiric alpha frequency changing from 9.2 at 12 years to the final 10.2/sec. (Some empiric data for the EEG assign slightly higher values to the EEG from 10.2 – 11/sec. This does not change the fact of the limit at 12-15 years of age.)

***The Table entitled "Auxiliary Table to Table VIII" presents the year by year detail in Factors A and B. The multiplication of the heart-value by Factors A and B yields the rather remarkable fact that in Table VIII (and the Auxiliary Table) can be seen the equation for linear growth (Heart x A x B) as an equation of motion "interlocked" with the overall Equation VIII as an equation for the "giant spiral" of our body structure and mass.

(Details of Factors A and B)

Age years	FACTOR A $\dfrac{TDM}{31.490255}$ +	$\dfrac{t}{G.S.R.}$	) x ($\dfrac{g^2}{(4.0091652)}$ +	FACTOR B Gender-Genital $\dfrac{Weight}{grams}$ x	$(0.040188 - K^{**}$ x Cate Ratio) per gram =	Product x Heart $\dfrac{}{gms}$ as in Table VIII.
Birth	4.518582 (5.2998334)	0.77 / 0.9859467	4.0091652	6.92154 (6.5896122)	0.372814**	= 34.923846 x 24.31 (848.99867)
½	5.9351649 (7.4887883)	1.27 / 0.8174439	4.0091652	11.0545 (5.6155527)	0.14918	= 42.053685 x 34.13 (1435.2922)
1	7.11966288 (9.0339485)	1.77 / 0.9246268	4.0091652	13.583 (5.3245429)	0.09684	= 48.101647 x 44.00 (2116.4747)
2	8.5048533 (12.833932)	2.77 / 0.639859	4.0091652	11.661 (4.6803723)	0.05756	= 60.067579 x 58.05 (3486.9227)
3	8.6375928 (15.199007)	3.77 / 0.5745712	4.0091652	12.529 (4.543527)	0.04265	= 69.05710 x 66.15 (4568.1271)
4	9.446068 (15.990468)	4.77 / 0.7288706	4.0091652	15.134 (4.8767173)	0.057779	= 77.980999 x 79.46 (6196.3695)
6	11.615339 (21.739561)	6.77 / 0.6686933	4.0091652	16.576 (4.4392626)	0.025947	= 96.507617 x 104.76 (10110.138)
8	14.004332 (27.199957)	8.77 / 0.6646142	4.0091652	17.838 (4.1777343)	0.00945	= 113.63419 x 133.54 (15174.709)
10	15.827118 (31.568481)	10.77 / 0.6841847	4.0091652	22.908 (4.0813254)	0.00315	= 128.84124 x 158.66 (20441.951)
12	17.672133 (37.47692)	12.77 / 0.6447936	4.0091652	18.699 (4.0282381)	0.00102	= 150.96594 x 175.02 (26422.06)
15	21.649872 (39.620308)	15.77 / 0.8775524	4.0091652	57.847 (4.0097436)	0.00001	= 158.86727 x 249.39 (39619.908)
18	23.10524 (37.341813)	18.77 / 1.3184352	4.0091652	67.379 (4.7833499)	0.01149	= 178.61895 x 273.42 (48837.993)

**K = 0.155889 but only 0.15588 is used except at 15 years of age when 0.15589 is used.

K is used only for the post-natal Catecholamine Ratio x 0.040188. At birth, the organism is at the end of the intra-uterine biomagnetic field.

Brief Discussion:

As I have tried to indicate, the concept of life-process growth pulsing, sentient, and genderizing—existing only because of a bioplasma dominated by biomagnetic interactions—in analogy with plasma physics—has a long history. It begins in the years 1936-1949, ending with *The Growth Concept of Nervous Integration*. There, my insistence upon the idea that the brain acted as a force of growth mediating its "directives" through the pituitary hormones to create a "potentiation-kinesis" equilibrium (*tension-relaxation equilibrium*) was met by the "absolute dictum" that there is no connection between brain and pituitary.* That monograph also contained the concept of renal hypertension as due to the same phenomenon—the Goldblatt clamp on the renal artery interpreted as a peripheral artificial experiment tantamount to a "natural" central effect; it affirmed also that the brain-mind was not merely a "chronologist" of "the conscious" but—in the unconscious—it acted as a "relativist" and that a dream was in all likelihood a four-dimensional phenomenon.

Any new development was now to meet the dramatic discovery of DNA's double helical structure. The scientific world turned—rightly—to the "miracles" of the important and still developing science of molecular biology, one of the really great discoveries of mankind.

Yet, twenty-five years have elapsed—and we are no nearer to a working concept that will help us in the battle against cancer, schizophrenia, heart attack and stroke, and the arthritides. Through molecular biology we now know—exquisitely—the *mechanics* of what we knew for a hundred years.

We knew and know that cells divide and somehow synthesize their proteins and take in oxygen and excrete waste and divide and multiply. And molecular biology still has many other discoveries *in the details of the mechanics of this process*. Perhaps a true science of "genetic engineering" will someday evolve.

But the *facts* of the past twenty-five years point to the idea that there is something *fundamental* to all these "magic mountains" and "industrial valleys" . . . That something is what DNA is immersed in and that something is what provides the vehicles for RNA "commuting." That something limits the growth of any particular cell of any particular species—and indeed as we have seen—determines the proportions of heart, brain, pulse, weight and adaptational

---

*In the history of theory, the Growth Concept of Nervous Integration takes precedence over even Geoffrey Harris (1954).
But for *proof* the world is indebted to Guillemin and to Schally.

power . . . And, most important, that something in some way is directed by the brain in a manner as if a "giant endocrine" constantly "commandeers" the pituitary to do its bidding in accord with a very specific set of mysterious laws.

From 1956-1976, these studies in the possibility of a bioplasma which functions on the basis of a "basic template" in all cells structured in relation to the arterial and heart system—their dynamic interplay determined by sets of biomagnetic fields capable of being (with enormous speed) communicated to the cells of the "giant endocrine" that is also a computer-composer of all inputs and outputs in the inner world of the body and the outer world of environment—this bioplasma has held the center of my interest. And in these brief pages, I have tried to state the major concepts, analogies, and equations of the bioplasma, its biomagnetic fields ordered in every cell in the body by those of the brain. And the larger the frontal and prefrontal-temporal area, the greater the power to "commandeer," to "compute and compose" and to "communicate"—so that only man finally builds the civilizations of history while "taming" the more primitive Self that knows only "kill or be killed."

If the paraconscious system indeed is the monitor protecting life-process by its computing-composing and mobilizing functions—and by its tension-discharging dreams, then the aphorism that may one day result from this work (amounting to a paradigm) is:

Every cell is a bioplasma (in the flux of life-process growth and repair) of pulse, sentience, and genderization. In one way or another, every cell's influence is in the final computations of our actions and in the final compositions of our dreams and our arts and our science . . . We are all of a piece.

The immediate practical task is to try to comprehend, establish, and put to use the biomagnetic hierarchical order of the bioplasma.

The practical consequences can be immediate.

* * * * * * * *

Consequences for Drug-Addiction, Drug-Testing, Toxicology and Immunology.

Once one becomes aware that there is a state of living matter that is more fundamental even than that operative in DNA transactions, such things as *drug-testing* will be immediatley involved. We shall perhaps know a little more of the dangerous "side-actions" of what is administered whether in hallucinogenic cults, neuroleptic drugs, anti-cancer irradiation, arterial "plaque" medications from mystical diets to cholesterol and lipid-lowering drugs . . . What role does the bioplasma play in the immune processes, in the auto-immune diseases, in the susceptibility to viruses of all kinds? . . .

Especially all addictions, all drug-tolerance come under new scrutiny. Anyone who has ever tried to "psychoanalyze" the drug-addict (alcoholic, barbiturate, tranquillizers, morphine, heroin, etc.)—*and the drug-addicts themselves*—knows that these drugs become as "necessary as breathing and more necessary than loving"—because, it is my conviction, these drugs have the power to insert themselves into the energy-transactions of the bioplasma, alter their biomagnetic interactions, doing much more than "reducing tension," and indeed practically supplanting while temporarily exciting genderizing-sexual transformations.

The theory of a bioplasma becomes of urgent importance here in all these "mysterious conditions." All the DNA mechanics in the world will not alter a single fact or feature of drug-addiction. And that is not to be laid at the door of the great science of molecular biology. Grappling with such problems as drug-addiction belongs to another science—that of the bioplasma itself . . . So too with the "business" of addicting vast populations to the tranquillizers and the neuroleptics because "we don't know their side-actions."

In a longer work, we plan a more full exposition of these attributes of the bioplasma in relation to the "disaster diseases."

We must now proceed to a final summary of the main points—and to certain matters reserved for a special *Appendix*, a quite separate volume, if it proves as valid as it appears now, on sheer mathematic grounds, to be.

* * * * * * * *

But there is one matter which must be briefly touched upon before we embark upon the summary. That matter has to do with the title of this work on life-process growth and the theory of the bioplasma under the aegis of "revolution in the body-mind."

It will be observed that we do not speak of the "mind-body" or the "psychosomatic" which has become a standard and generally useless "cliché." Instead, we use the word "body" as the adjective in the phrase "body-mind." And that is because our concept of growth as life-process growth pulsing, sentient, and genderizing is inseparable from the concept of the bioplasma capable of supporting and propagating specific frequencies in a milieu dominated by electromagnetic field interactions . . . "*Body*-mind"—because the bioplasma of the *body* serves the brain-heart—because the brain-heart monitor as computer-composer of *body-first and world-second* in its creative defense and in its dreams expresses the *body first* and the world second—even though world and body are constantly amalgamating images—; *"body"* because, as Freud tried to teach the world, *the Ego is "first and foremost a body Ego"*—*"body"* because that free-flowing sexual energy is first of the body and makes its impact upon the sexual-sentient as well as on the sexual-sublimating brain in the constant paradox between the drives to preserve the body and the drives to sexual perpetuation of the species. But most important, *most cogent because the language of life-process pulsing, sentient, and genderizing in every cell of body, brain and heart is actually*—despite the hatreds and jealousies and bigotry and sheer infuriated mediocrity and immense ignorance of the superstition-ridden peoples who are "anti-Freudian"—*the language of life-process growth and of the biomagnetic hierarchy of the bioplasma from body to brain-heart is the "root-language" of the famous Freudian "unconscious."*

We may prejudice our case in the eyes of the "esoteric experts on growth" who are constantly making formulae for growth based on dead cell-number and dead mass—sexuality not even existing—but we are compelled by our convictions to state that the language of the bioplasma was first "spoken"—without his knowing it fully—by Freud, when he had to try to explain how it was that an "unconscious" could exist even though nobody knew how.

The language of the bioplasma—and of life-process pulsing, sentient, and genderizing—first appeared as the Freudian language of metapsychology.

Today, we are in a position to begin to develop that "root-language" or, as the German tongue has it—that "Ursprache"— toward the precise nature of the bioplasma and its biomagnetic hierarchies which can bring order into the chaos and frustration of our attempts to deal with cancer, schizophrenia, heart attack and stroke.

From 1936-1949, I began to try to create a "developmental neurology" to go hand in hand with the discovery of "developmental psychology."

It has been a long journey. But I think the goal may be in sight.

Freud taught:

Men are strong as long as they follow a strong idea. They become powerless when they desert it.

The solution to the famous Freudian goal "The Project" is, I think, because of the concepts of this work, not too far down the road.

We are not concerned, though it is sometimes useful to have books constantly reviewing and rehashing Freud's "Project" (cf. Pribram and Gill[9]), with the verbiage of re-iteration and iteration and re-iteration again.

Summary

(1) The basic concepts and the outline of a new science—the science of the bioplasma—is presented here coupled with the definition of life-process as life-process growth pulsing, sentient, and genderizing.

(2) This takes the "problem of growth" out of the hands of all those theorists and makers of "growth formulae" based on essentially dead numbers of cells encased in inert dimensions. It puts the nature of meaningful life-process growth into the world of modern physics and biophysics.

(3) The concept of the bioplasma—which puts the DNA-RNA mechanisms and manufactures at a central area and pivot of the bioplasma—is broader and more basic than the basis of molecular biology. Because of the nature of a bioplasma—in its analogy to plasma physics—it is our concept that it is the bioplasma hierarchy that—from cell through artery to heart-brain—shapes and limits as it modifies the activity of the DNA-RNA in every tissue. It does this because a bioplasma is dominated by electromagnetic field interactions, i.e. paramagnetic.

(4) The concept of the bioplasma as used here includes its capacity, by analogy with the magnetic mirror effect, of creating a shaping, limiting resistance to life-process growth.

(5) The concept of the bioplasma—as in plasma physics—includes its capacity to support oscillations and to propagate oscillations, e.g. the "brainwave" and the "EKG" of the heart. It is here conceived that every species has its brain-heart and brain-cord ratio (as has been known for many decades) and also its own characteristic ratio between the net oscillation frequencies of its body cells in relation to the oscillation frequencies of heart and brain.

(6) In studies from 1936 to 1976, it has been shown that there is an image of the beating heart and throbbing artery however subliminally within the brain-mind. But this is not to be confused with very specific information from each cell communicated via the circulation (as "travelling transducer") to the brain's arteries and the brain cells. As part of these studies, there evolved the concept of a monitor—a computing-composing monitor—part of the life-process "protective barrier" first put forth by Sigmund Freud; we have named this monitor *the paraconscious system of brain-body and body-mind transformations* of energy including the relativistic phenomena of dreams, as well as of conscious insight.

(7) In a certain sense, it may be said that *every cell in the body dreams*. This matter is of importance in discerning the fore-warning

cancer and heart-attack dreams described.

(8) There are two great "body-mind" consequences of this approach to life-process growth pulsing, sentient, and genderizing as inseparable from the bioplasma. The *first* is "physical"—the *second* "mental-emotional." The first states that our concept of the artery must change from that of a "pipeline" to that of a mosaic of cells—a surface and a mass—also of the bioplasma and quantitatively differentiated to be "equal" to the totality of basic template synthesis in every cell. Should this "equality" be destroyed either by arterial cell disease or by basic template disturbance or abnormality, the disbalance will be "communicated" via the circulation to the brain-heart and to the "monitor" which operates by controlling a biomagnetic field hierarchy in the brain. In turn, the brain—capable of acting as a "giant endocrine"—we now know can influence the pituitary to send a "biomagnetic delegate" ("hormone") or to refurbish those "delegates" already "resident" in the distant "colonies" of organ tissue cells. . . . I believe that these communications are made feasible *through electron-transfer changes in the biomagnetic fields of blood-pigment cells themselves*—which instantly are capable of altering the charge upon them.*

(9) The second consequence in the "mental-emotional" sphere is that we may achieve new and more precise terms for *the mechanisms of the unconscious* which Freud could only describe in the "fore-runner language of metapsychology." Here then is the road to the solution of Freud's famous "Project" about which there is continuing verbigeration in articles and books containing no ` concept for its elucidation in modern measurable terms . . . The historic contumely heaped upon Freud by the religious "guardians of the soul" and the arrogant neurologists and misinformed and ignorant populations were all based on neurology and the brain as a set of railroad "paths" and "areas"—"railroad stations" . . . But Freud was called upon, by his own genius and the facts, to study what it was in the "railroad bed" that "tore up the tracks" . . . The rest is history among the Philistines.

(10) As a result we find that in all the equations presented here the factors of "Gender Force" and "Gender-Genital (Reproductive) Mass" are essential portions of the activity of the bioplasma.

(11) It is the concept of this work that the bioplasma is a reality which will be discovered and measured—particularly in the cells of brain and heart where very large and very obvious oscillations are both supported and propagated. Because of these facts it is not impossible

---

*All these characteristics make possible the concept of the arterial system as a "travelling transducer."

that it will be of "liquid form" and even that it may be *luminescent* (not incandescent) when it is discovered. Luminescence is defined as a characteristic non-thermal emission of electromagnetic radiation by a specific material upon excitation. (It is also called "phosphorescent" derived from the Greek meaning of the word "bearer of light.") The luminescent process involves (1) absorption of energy; (2) excitation; and (3) emission of energy usually in the form of electromagnetic radiation in the visible portion of the spectrum.* Those who have read the text of this report know that the equations—now to be summarized as to their salient features—contain the electromagnetic radiation frequency of electron paramagnetic resonance (EPR) namely 2.8026x 10^6 cycles/sec/gauss . . . In this manner, in an unbroken line of studies from the 1936-1949 period to now, we have kept at the concept of the brain as an electromotive force of biomagnetic life-process growth pulsing, sentient, and genderizing . . .

The equations of bioplasma life process growth are these:

Equation I: illustrates the species and individual primacy of the brain-heart relationship in life-process growth; develops the life-process maintenance constant as 0.040188 and from that extracts the concept and values of the basic template (TDM_{basic}) of value of 727.59 grams at 18 years of age in relation to total body weight of 61556 grams—a force acting along the length of each base pair of the double helix or 3.4 Angström; creates the basis for the translation of 0.040188 x Catecholamine Ratio per gram into the major oscillations of the bioplasma—namely the EEG, the EKG and the here discovered G.F.f. Its denominator contains the basic brain-heart field dimensions and amounts to C^4 cancelling out the C^4 in the numerator. (cf. Appendix for derivation.)

Equation II: bases the synthesis of body mass specifically as per the electromagnetic radiation frequency of 2.8026 cycles per second/per gauss thus demanding the establishment of a species-specific bioplasma net body-cell oscillation in specific proportion to the heart pulse. (Equation VI establishes the same phenomena for the various species studied—and need not be further summarized here.) Equation II includes the relationship between pulse and length of the body—a matter of ultimate importance to synthesis of mass along the *length* of the double helix. It illustrates the "cancer" weight-loss.

Equations III and III (A): created by equating I and II quite simply brings together the species characteristics of brain, heart,

*Cf. The Kirlian photographic phenomenon of bioluminescence, under magnetic fields, in human tissue and plant chlorophyll.

Catecholamine Ratio/gm., length and pulse in a relationship expressed by the species constant: 1.829775. Equation III is further refined in the Appendix.*

Equation IV: embraces the TDM (basic *tissue differenting mass* or "template") and illustrates the manner by which the cord-body and the cord-brain weight relationships evolved (both as parts of IV.) The formulation of IV (A) illustrates the two fractions of TDM$_{basic}$ IV (B) illustrates the principle of heart-artery mass equivalence to total basic TDM at any time. It is the basis for our new concept of the artery and (as will be further described in a later communication) the concept of the red-pigment of the blood-cell as carrying changes in the biomagnetic energy balance between body and heart, between body and brain, between cell and artery. Subject to all the laws of cellular bioplasma, the arterial lining cells—and the tissue immediately under the lining—are capable of growing the deadly neoplasms of familial xanthomatosis. IV (B) brings into view sharply the concept that different biomagnetic fields come into play from conception to post-natal death. *The law of the relationship of these fields is part of the emerging science of longevity*. It is our concept that the brain functions by its control of a series of such fields structured as a hierarchy and mediated by a central "computer-composer" of the body-mind (the *paraconscious*). IV (C) illustrates the fact that from the moment of conception there is a separate "apportionment" of that which goes to body-heart and that which goes to gender-genital-reproductive equipment. The result of this formulation is again confirmatory of the TDM$_{basic}$ thus derived and at the same time yielding the first equation for the growth of adrenal-gonad-genital equipment in history.

Equation V: returns to the Catecholamine Ratio/gram and shows the detail of the Gender Force factor (G.F.f) including its incremental growth and its percentage incremental growth the latter so dramatic in its relationship to the age-incidence of schizophrenia as illustrated in Figure 5.

Equation VI: has already been summarized above.

Equation VII: represents the bioplasma solution for heat-production in which again two biomagnetic fields operate: the first from birth to 3-4 years, the second thereafter to 18 years. (A third field may come into play at 12 years of age directed toward the sudden efflorescence of gender-genital growth. This third field must be left for a later report.)

*There the constant becomes that of bioplasma gravitational interaction.

Two forms of Equation VII are: *the first* in its entire complexity which introduces the concept of a *Systems Distribution Divisor* acting in relationship to the two different fields as they affect the constant $84.784758 = C^4 + g^2$ numerically multiplied by the two different biomagnetic field values. *The second* simplifies the S.D.D to a constant easier to handle. Into the equation for heat-production enters the G.F.f. as already noted—acting conservingly in the first 4-6 years of life.

Equation VIII: presents the culmination of the concept of the bioplasma dominated by the specific brain-cord-heart species proportions in every cell in the body. Of especial interest are Factors A and B as noted in the Auxiliary Table to Table VIII. Factor A shows the structure of the basic template in relation to the heart—including the Gender Shaping Ratio—increasing after 12 years of age through the 15-18 year period.

In addition, Factor A illustrates the combined value of the frequency of EPR squared x g^2 in the denominator of the TDM_{basic}. Factor B is the measure of the variation of the basic template and again includes g^2 plus the gender-genital mass multiplied by the Catecholamine Ratio x 0.040188/grams. Detailed discussion of these variables is reserved for a later report. It is to be noted that while brain and cord each have their coefficients, the only coefficient the heart has is the product of Factors A and B. Since the total equation is that of the "giant spiral" which is our body, the heart x Factor A x Factor B resolves into a linear equation of motion joined to the "giant spiral." The further consequences of this joining also must be postponed.

We have now concluded the task of barely "listing" the equations of the bioplasma (save Equation IX). Finally we emphasize that *life-process growth, pulsing, sentient, and genderizing* in the various species, each with its unique kind of bioplasma, *is life-process.*

August 29, 1976
East Hampton, Long Island
New York.

Daniel E. Schneider, M.D.

Appendix

Notes on:

1. *New Horizons for the Science of the Mind—Conjunction of Scientists*

2. *Derivation of Equation I and Development of Equation IX—The Brain-Mind Equation (with Table IX)*

3. *The Circulating Blood as a Circulating Bioplasma Set of Brain-Mind Informing Biomagnetic Fields...The Age-Old Problem of Drug-Addiction and a Research Project Considering Bioplasma Theory and New Techniques to Neutralize Drug Need.*

4. *"Heart Attack and Stroke Personality" as Secondary to Genetic Disease of Arteries Akin to Familial Xanthomatosis..."Type A Personality" as a Fundamentally Erroneous Concept.*

5. *Final Definition of "Life-Process" as Life-Process Growth, Pulsing, Sentient, and Genderizing...The Constant Validating of the Freudian View in Modern Biophysical Terms.*

6. *Equation III as the Gravitational Interaction Equation Illustrating The Principle of Mirror-Image Symmetry in Cell-Division and in the Formation of the Double Helix. (Preliminary Report)*

Brief Comment on:

7. *The New Work (1976) by Albert Szent-Györgyi: Electron Biology and Cancer—A New Theory of Cancer"*

These concepts, their equations, and tables have been put together over the many years in the faith that the time would come when they would have at least exploratory if not experimental validity and lead along a logical line to new clinical horizons in the appreciation of the "giant endocrine computer-composer para-conscious" power of the human brain as it is constantly transformed into "mind" by the body itself, and then—activating itself in the outer world—"building its own stately mansions."—its architectural-musical-mathematic rhythms.

Several additional considerations must now be quite simply out-lined in anticipation of the later full development soon to be devoted to various clinical and again mathematic bioplasma aspects of the new horizons which we envision for the science of the mind and for the longevity of its body. These include the derivation for our Equation I and the ultimate equation for the brain—Equation IX and Table IX, thus accentuating their importance and their "embrace" of the implications of all the other precedent equations and tables.

But anterior to that, let us make the following points:

(1) A new science—a new *neuromental* science, if you will—should result from the concepts of this work—a science in which many branches of knowledge, expertise and experience may join forces each playing its role. In this respect I think we must give up the old term "psycho-somatic"—once so useful—but rather barren as time has gone on. In its place—leaving its "conglomerate, waste-basket, or blanket" glibness—we must put the following separate fields:

(a) *The science of body-mind signalling and transformational activities* by which we mean that every cell in the body reports via the biomagnetic field relationships between the "basic template" of every cell, the blood cell flowing to and from its cell-boundaries back to heart-lung-heart and thence to brain-arteries and body-arteries which are always at stress "just before the capillary bridge." Here in the protein synthesis of the basic tissue differentiating template, the great science of molecular biology holds a pivotal place though not an exclusive one.

(b) Classical and newer neurologic scientists will have a role in discerning and developing the concept of the paraconscious monitor by recognizing that it is the "super-integral" of the integrating activities of the neuronal pre-frontal lobe and the integrations of the sonic-acoustic temporal lobe. In our studies of the paraconscious, from the clinical psychiatric as well as in the phenomena of heart attack and cancer (cf. below), the evidence shows that the prefrontal and temporal lobe (sonic-acoustic) have a mutual "cross-reference" system of incredible complexity and virtuosity. It is as though the prefrontal receives the "alert-alarm" fibers of the "mixer" reticular activating system (RAS) together with the quieter, cooler, firm computations of the conceptual parietal areas, while the temporal lobe system determines whether to "cry terror, sing love, or dictate law." As we have already stated in our book on the psychoanalysis of heart attack, there is evidence to suggest that injury or shock to this system in childhood may play a role in the disintegration of the arterial intima at the classical stress-points. Similar injury or shock—all through human history, myth and legend—may suddenly disrupt the conduction system of the heart which is *the bioplasma* supporting and propagating its "EKG" on which our lives depend.

(c) It is quite obvious then that the hematologist might begin to look upon the amazing pigment of red blood cells as capable of electron transfer and of carrying biomagnetic charges—and hence needs to be refurbished every twenty-four hours. Here is a direct relationship between *daily maintenance growth and the biomagnetic field interplay.*

(d) A similar consideration—but not identical—bears upon the processes of immunity as *centrally controlled,* by a constant brain-heart field. (Cf. my original paper, [together with C.C. Clarke] in 1937 on the electro-encephalocardiogram[10] as evidence that there is indeed a "working brain-heart center.")

As part of the new neuro-mental science thus inadequately outlined, there will, I think, arise *the law for the changing sequence of biomagnetic fields* which must be maintained for longevity to increase. Here is an area in which the pure mathematician and physicist will hold absolute sway. If as I suspect there is a supervening law of biomagnetic field succesion and sequence, it would be built upon life-span divisions such as are already indicated by our equations as presented here, namely (a) an *intrauterine field* changing sharply at birth; (b) post-natal *myelinizing* field completing the "insulation" of the nervous system between 3-4 years and co-inciding with the Gender Force factor changing from negative to positive by 6-7 years; (c) a specific gender-sexual field beginning sharply at 12 and responsible for the enormous efflorescence of gender-genital equipment and characteristics from 15 to 18 years. It endures until 32 years of age when *heart attack* in the male and *cancer of the uterus* in the female begins to make its appearance rising to great intensity of incidence for 13 years at least until 45 years of age; (d) from 45 years of age to at least 75 years of age there is a steady diminution (by present standards) of physical power but with even increasing mental power in varying periods of this phase; and finally from 75 years onward in states of existence that we are only now beginning to discern and differentiate carrying with them the potential of life-spans far beyond 100 years of age—how far is a matter of proper record-keeping.

The sequence and building of these fields, which are "stacked" one on "top" of the other, again suggest an architecture that "rings bells" like Giotto's *Bell Tower* in Florence, Italy. But it also suggests the presence of *time-transformational laws.* In *The Growth Concept of Nervous Integration* (1949) I suggested that the "mind" is not a conscious "chronologist" but is also equipped with a *relativist* "unconscious" that is able to store material not in relation to the sequence of events but in relation to time-intensity dimension. It is the "machinery" of such storage that contains and holds back the repressed that makes possible the stability of the sense of reality. When this is "fractured," the "repressed returns" as hallucinations and delusions. This is another reason why the Gender Force factor of Figure 5 is as dramatic a "lead" as it is. It suggests that the disease in schizophrenia is as "dissociative" in the mental sphere as is cancer in the physical body-sphere, both based on the disruption of the necessary biomagnetic "electron clockwork" in the bioplasma.

An even greater role will emerge for that "psychoanalyst" properly trained in the evaluation of the new body-mind aphorism that—on net balance—*every cell in the body dreams*—if one understands the heart-arterial as a "travelling transducer" system in relation to cell on one hand and to the paraconscious computer-composer on the other.

(2) We must now revert to the derivation of Equation I and to the final equation—Equation IX—for the brain.

Development of Equation I:

The equation is developed on the concept that the brain and the heart each are synthesized—according to our concept of the bioplasma—by the presence of electric charges in free space and therefor will obey Coulomb's Law (Electrostatics) that the force between two point (electric) charges in free space is a pure attraction or repulsion and is given by

$$\text{Force} = \frac{q_1 \times q_2}{4\pi \, \epsilon_o r^2} \text{ newtons}$$

where q_1 and q_2 are the magnitudes of the charges in coulombs, where r is their separation in meters and where ϵ is the constant of "permittivity" in free space, (measured in farads/meter.) In certain systems, a constant K must be—or is as a convenience—included in the numerator. But in distinction to the electrostatic systems are the *electromagnetic* systems which start with *the law of attraction between currents*—and this is applicable to the bioplasma concept in which the bioplasma is dominated by *electromagnetic* interactions. Its dimensions differ from that of the electrostatic by a factor which has the dimension of a speed. This relationship between currents is connected with the fact that the ratio of the constants (technically given as $2K_e/K_m$) must have the value of *square of the speed of light*, or C^2, in any consistent system of units. The units in this electromagnetic system (emu) are translatable into ($cms^{1/2}gms^{1/2}$) the square of which is cms-gms, in which our equations deal.

We therefor conceive that one such field—the brain-field—set to work by the "promote"—go—stop "program" of the double helix—will synthesize a set of masses in intervals of time—as will also the heart field. Or, the work of the fields may be given as:

$\text{Brain}_{gms} = (m_1 + m_2 + m_3 \ldots m_n)C^2$, and so too the heart $\text{Heart}_{gms} = (m_1 + m_2 + m_3 \ldots m_n)C^2$

Next, our bioplasma concept demands the sentience of neuronal conductivity, using the catecholamine *dopamine* which breaks down into *homovanillic acid* (HVA), and the pulsing of heart-polarization which demands the adrenalines breaking down into metanephrine (M) + normetanephrine (NM).

This creates the Catecholamine Ratio (for which there is empiric data as noted). Therefore HVA/gm. is taken in ratio to $(M+NM)/gm.^2$ since the latter two quantities (M+NM) represents the product of precursors obeying the algebraic rule of $(a-b)^2/gm.^2$ where in the $(a^2 - 2ab + b^2)$ the $-2ab$ for all practical purposes is negligible, and vanishing.

Therefore the Catecholamine Ratio (before cancelling out by factors in the denominator of the gms^2 in the numerator) is

$$\frac{HVA}{(M+NM)_{gms.}} \times gms.^2$$

So too the constant of life-process growth maintenance is $\text{TDM}_{basic\text{-}18\,yrs.}$ per total body weight at 18 years or 727.59 gms/61556 gms. which is multiplied by the length of each base-pair of the double helix or 3.4×10^{-8} cms. thus creating the constant 0.040188 cms x 10^{-8} representing the total maintenance constant in helical base-pair units.

The numerator of Equation I—before cancellation out of the $gms.^2$ in the Catecholamine Ratio—and before the cancelling out of the *cms.* x 10^{-8} in the life-process maintenance constant is as follows:

$$0.040188_{cms.} \times 10^{-8}(\text{Brain}_{gms.} \times \text{Heart}_{gms.}) \frac{HVA \times gms.^2}{(M+NM)\ gms.}$$

The denominator indicates the modification of the electrostatic by the biomagnetic thus:

(a) The quantity $(4\pi)^2$ is phrased as *per* the gyromagnetic constant of 2.00229 in the phenomena of electron paramagnetic resonance or 157.9144/2.00229 = 78.866897.

(b) The two "r's" of the electrostatic fields become the square of the length of 46 chromosomes x 4 cms.* or (186 cms.$\frac{3}{2}$ x gms. $\frac{1}{2}$ x sec-^{2})^2 or 33856 cms^3 gms. sec-^{4}. Here the units are in terms of the current doing work per gram$^{1/2}$ per sec of synthesis for each strand, and, squared, this becomes grams/sec^2.

Hence the total formulation in terms of DNA helix at work along both the "up and down staircase" of both strands at the same time becomes:

$$\frac{33856 \text{ cms.}^3 \text{ gms. sec}^{-4}}{\text{gms. sec}^{-2}} = 33856 \text{ cms.}^3 \text{ sec}^{-2}$$

as representing synthesizing current intensity per gram per second per cell.

(c) The ratio of *magnetic dipole moment to potential difference* expressive of the relative permittivity and permeability is given in the same *emu* (electromagnetic unit) system as 10-^{6} sec-^{2}/cms.^{2}.

(d) The unit of work is therefore, in gram-force units, equivalent to Joules, (1.0197 gms.cms^2/sec^2)^2, or, 1.039788 gms^{2}cms^4/sec^4.

(e) The number of cells, in a body weight of 61556 gms., using a specific gravity of 1.1484 x 10-^{2} micra, is 5.391360 x 10^{12}. Watson[13] in his book on the molecular biology of the gene estimates that the human body contains "upwards of 5000 billion cells"—a figure with which our result is in adequate agreement. And (5.391390 x 10^{12})^2 = 29.066762 x 10^{24}.

The denominator of Equation I thus becomes, placed beneath the numerator already delineated:

Equation I:

$$\frac{\text{Body}}{\text{Weight}_{\text{gms.}}} = \frac{0.040188 \text{ cms. x } 10^{-8} \text{ (Brain x Heart)}_{\text{gms.}}^2 \text{ x } \frac{\text{HVA x gms.}^2}{(M+NM)_{\text{gms.}}} \text{ x C}^4}{(78.866897) \frac{(10^{-6} \text{ sec}^2)}{\text{cms.}^2} \frac{(33856 \text{ cms}^3)}{\text{sec}^2} (29.066762 \text{ x } 10^{24})(1.039788 \text{ x gms.}^2 \frac{\text{cm}^4}{\text{sec}^4} \text{ x } 10^8)}$$

and since C^4 = 8.07 cms^4 x 10^{41}, then if taken together with 10-^{8}, the net for the numerator with *cms.* of the constant and the gm^2 of the Catecholamine Ratio cancelled out, is: 8.07 x 10^{33} *cms^4*.

And since the denominator—multiplied out and its units

*Cf. Crick, F.H.C.[12]

cancelling—amounts to 8.0699684 x 10^{33} *cms*^{4} we arrive at the net result for Equation I:

$$\text{Body Weight}_{gms.} = 0.040188 \, (\text{Brain x Heart})_{gms}{}^2 \times \frac{\text{HVA}}{(\text{M+NM})_{gms.}}$$

which is the "relativity equation" only in the sense that it is the equation of the enormous speeds of the double helix at work in the bioplasma milieu dominated by electromagnetic interactions and by the limiting force of the brain-heart "center control" in every species.

$$* \; * \; * \; * \; * \; * \; * \; *$$

It is from Equation I that we derive what we consider the only meaningful equation for the growth of the brain, illustrating its control of the major oscillations of life-process "sweeping" along the spiralling formulation for the cord the spiral exponent of which gives us body weight. And as will be seen in the equation below—Equation IX—the brain exercises this "sweep" *per* the body pulse *and* the G.F.f. (sexual gender force) as it modifies the basic tissue template of every cell and the gender-genital mass of reproductive chemistry and physiology *in which every cell of the body participates*—precisely as Sigmund Freud observed in his concepts of the life-protective forces of the soma and the "reproductive instincts" *fused* to those life-protective forces even though in the end the soma dies and the species goes on.

In Equation IX—and Table IX—I have tried to arrange the values involved for eventual practical work in the laboratory and in future "computer-composer" analysis.

Equation IX. Brain Weight as Brain Control of Bioplasma and Life-Process Growth

From Equation I:

$$\text{Brain Weight}_{gms.} = \frac{\text{Body Weight}_{gms.}}{0.040188 \; \text{Catecholamine Ratio/gm. x Heart Weight}_{gms.}}$$

From Equation IV:

$$\text{Body Wt.}_{gms.} = \text{Cord Wt.}_{gms.} \times (\text{Spiral Exponent} = (0.2\pi + 0.1e + 0.08t) \times 10^3$$

From Equation I (illustrated in Figure 2-B) and Equation V:

$$\frac{0.040188 \; \text{Catecholamine Ratio}}{\text{gm.}} = \frac{\text{Pulse/sec + G.F.f.}}{(\text{alpha frequency})_{gms.}}$$

From Equation IV (C):

$$\text{Heart}_{gms.} = \frac{\text{TDM}_{basic\text{-}gms.} + 2.8026\ (\text{Pulse/sec})\ \text{Gender-Genital Weight}_{gms.}}{2.8026\ (\text{Pulse/sec.})}$$

Now, substituting:

$$\text{Brain Weight}_{gms.} = \frac{\text{alpha frequency}(2.8026)(\text{Pulse/sec})(\text{Cord x Spiral Exponent})_{gms.}}{(\text{Pulse/sec} + \text{G.F.f.})\big[(\text{TDM}_{basic\text{-}gms} + 2.8026\ (\text{Pulse/sec})(\text{G-G})_{gms.})\big]}$$

where G-G$_{gms.}$ stands for *that component in every cell in the body which is devoted to the sum total of factors going into the establishment of gender-genital equipment,* together with and part of such phenomena as the androgen / estrogen ratios.

As already stated, Table IX has been designed for Equation IX values for future experimental research in practical laboratory work.

* * * * * * * *

But, we must observe that Equation IX for the growth of the brain is the first of its kind.

It is based on the theory of the bioplasma. It is designed to illuminate the operation supporting brain-mind transformations in particular in relation to all those mental phenomena now known to be related to the alpha and other frequencies of the brain during varying mental states, and during waking as opposed to sleeping, and during alert-alarm states as well as to dreams.

This way, I believe, lies the future in the study of the body-mind.

* * * * * * * *

(3) It will by now be clear that the so-called "circulating blood and its plasma" must be re-considered as a true bioplasma which has the peculiarity—in contrast to the "fixed" tissue of organs supplied—of being a "travelling" set of biomagnetic fields. As a tissue itself, it is "bounded" by the basic "template" of all tissues in relation to the containing surface of the intimal lining of the arteries, themselves under the acoustic forces of pulsation in blood-propulsion as well as under the bioplasma forces of the intimal cells. It now can be seen that *the "circulation" is as powerful an informant (to the brain-mind) of "internal imagery of feeling" as the nerves themselves are informative (with bio-feedback) of the outer world, and the objects and concepts of reality.* The circulation appears as a "travelling transducer."

This has led us to re-consider the entire age-old problem of drug-

TABLE IX

Age years	(Col. 1) 2.8026 x Pulse/sec (gms) x alpha freq. x Spiral Exp. (Body Weight)	(Col. 2) cord gms. (Col. 1 x Col. 2 = Numerator Eq. IX) gms.^{2}	(Col. 3) Pulse/sec + G.F.f.	(Col. 4) TDM$_{basic}$-gms + (2.8026 x Pulse/sec x Gend.-Gen. Wt. gms) gms. (Col. 3 x Col. 4 = Denominator Eq. IX)	Brain Weight (gms.) Eq. IX / Eq. I
Birth	2.8026 x 2.92 x 1.85 (3.82158 x 900.15) (15.139645) (3440) Numerator = 52080.378		0.6897615 x	(142.30 + 56.643094) = 198.94309 Denominator = 137.22328	379.5302 / 379.53
½	2.8026 x 2.89 x 5.10 (8.04127 x 940.15) (41.307521) (7560) Numerator = 312284.85		1.555806 x	(186.90 + 89.536399) = 276.43639 Denominator = 430.08139	726.1064 / 726.10
1	2.8026 x 2.63 x 6.55 (10.26373 x 980.15) (48.278988) (10060) Numerator = 485686.61		1.655316 x	(224.20 + 100.11669) = 324.31669 Denominator = 536.8466	904.7028 / 904.72
2	2.8026 x 2.06 x 7.70 (11.77196 x 1060.15) (44.454841) (12480) Numerator = 554796.41		1.643488 x	(267.82 + 67.323304) = 335.1433 Denominator = 550.80399	1007.2483 / 1007.27
3	2.8026 x 1.81 x 8.30 (12.90268 x 1140.15) (42.103459) (14711) Numerator = 619383.98		1.647799 x	(272 + 63.559498) = 335.55943 Denominator = 552.93449	1120.1760 / 1120.19
4	2.8026 x 1.65 x 8.30 (13.71962 x 1220.15) (38.381607) (16740) Numerator = 642508.1		1.5091641 x	(297.46 + 69.985992) = 367.44599 Denominator = 554.53629	1158.6403 / 1158.64

6
2.8026 x 1.48 x 9.10 (15.61859 x 1380.15)   1.5038314 x (365.77 + 68.545676 = 434.31367)   1245.7409
(37.745416) (21556)   Denominator = 653.13754   1245.14
Numerator = 813640.18

8
2.8026 x 1.36 x 9.20 (17.44440 x 1540.15)   1.463076 x (441.00 + 67.99208 = 508.99208)   1265.1124
(35.066131) (26867)   Denominator = 744.69409   1265.13
Numerator = 942121.74

10
2.8026 x 1.31 x 9.20 (19.2423 x 1700.15)   1.44348 x (498.40 + 84.105269 = 582.50526)   1310.7704
(33.776935) (32630)   Denominator = 840.83469   1310.74
Numerator = 1102141.3

12
2.8026 x 1.27 x 9.20 (20.9639 x 1860.15)   1.52398 x (556.50 + 66.449028 = 622.94902)   1345.0577
(32.745578) (38996)   Denominator = 949.36184   1345.11
Numerator = 1276946.5

15
2.8026 x 1.27 x 10.20 (24.90298 x 2100.15)   1.589976 x (681.76 + 205.89433 = 887.65433)   1345.3406
(36.30488) (52300)   Denominator = 1411.349   1345.34
Numerator = 1898745.2

18
2.8026 x 1.26 x 10.20 (26.30430 x 2340.15)   1.707072 x (727.59 + 237.9326 = 965.52260)   1345.2033
(36.019015) (61556)   Denominator = 1648.2165   1345.24
Numerator = 2217186.4

Nota bene: Equation IX answers and Table IX illustrates the long sought solution to why the brain weight grows so rapidly from birth to 1 year of age. Here the *power of the G.F.f.* (cf. Column 3 above) *is the answer. Negative up to 6 years of age it diminishes the denominator accordingly.* Without Equation I and the conversion of 0.040188 x Catecholamine Ratio per gram into the oscillatory frequency equivalents, the G.F.f. would not have been discovered.

Nota bene: Precisely the same power of the *G.F.f.* is indirectly involved in the Systems Distribution Divisor of Equation VII for heat-production per kilo because of the great rate of the brain made possible by the action of the G.F.f. just cited. And, later in the S.D.D., the rise in the gender-genital component gives the heat/kilo its distinctive curve under the aegis of Field II.
The G.F.f. acts in Equation VII *directly* also from birth to 6 years of age functioning as a *conserving force* per (alpha frequency + t). Thus, without the G.F.f. and the Gender-Genital components, the solution to the problem of human growth—on the basis of the theory of the bioplasma and on the basis of the definition of life-process as life-process growth pulsing and sentient—without the G.F.f. and the Gender-Genital component, these equations could not have come to fruition. Again—strange though it may seem to the uninformed—the observations of Sigmund Freud and the original "language" of metapsychology—*prove to be correct mathematically!*

D.E.S.

addiction in this light and to search out new methods of neutralizing "drug-need" which registers itself as "drug-level lowering" in the blood.

(4) On the basis of all the equations and all our previous clinical studies it seems apparent to us that the so-called "heart attack and stroke personality" (which we described from 1953-1956 culminating in the description in the book *The Image of the Heart* of "coronary character") recently highly advertised as Type A Personality is a snare and a delusion. *The primary disease is in the artery and in the paraconscious heart-brain monitors*—and the "hard-driving coronary type" which dies before 45-52 years of age is very clearly *a secondary compensation.* The "personality" of heart-attack men of the very early variety is thus one of tremendous inner insecurity on a fundamental arterial-paraconscious basis. It is a disease which runs in families— and, we believe, for all its secondary *raging,* is akin to the deadly disease of familial xanthomatosis,*—the little yellow tumors springing from the arterial wall and as capable of killing a child of 10 as its 45 year old father ...The sheer mental processes of such men fit the picture of such emotional inferiority. They have a tendency to project the consequences of the inner disease in a manner suggesting the Quixotic tendency to tilt at inimical windmills ... It is for this reason that I consider the "Type A Personality" as a *primary* cause of heart attack to be a fundamentally erroneous concept.

* * * * * * * *

(5) On the basis of these equations—as especially indicated in the final "brain-mind equation" (Equation IX), it is clear that our definition of "life-process" fits the early courageous vision of Sigmund Freud though it may one day re-orient the language of metapsychology his observation of the *facts of mental life* forced him to design.

Life-process is life-process growth, pulsing, sentient, and genderizing from the moment of conception to the moment of death.

The bioplasma is at one and the same time its milieu and its instrument in the "bioplasma kinship" of the seven different systems of the living body.**

*The brilliant work of Benditt already referred to showing mutant and mobile smooth muscle cells in the arterial plaque appeared in February 1977, six months after this was written.

Benditt's work is consonant entirely with our concept of the artery but he does not consider brain-heart monitoring factors.

**The present era of research is one filled with similar concepts trying to orient human consciousness and physiology to modern physics. Cf. recent note in *Science News,* vol.

(6) *Equation III as the Gravitational Interaction Equation Illustrating the Principle of Mirror-Image Symmetry in Cell-Division and in the Formation of the Double Helix, (Preliminary Report)*

If we look back at Equation III, the constant 13.59894 attracts our attention for a number of reasons to be postponed for a later full report. Here we may at once notice that if 13.59894 is divided by the Gravitation Constant 6.67 x 10-8, the result is 2.0388215 x 10⁸.

This immediately suggests a gravitation-interaction equation as would be logically expected from every cell division—all the daughter cells as we know exhibiting a certain amount of cohesion which ultimately, as differentiation goes on, becomes a *tissue.* (There are of course many other forces of cohesion.)

However we know that the body is built upon a plan of merged mirror-image symmetry so that the mass of each side may be expressed by its square root—and both multiplied together amounting to body mass as we know it.

The principle of symmetry begins when the male 23 chromosomes and the female 23 chromosomes intertwine around their central axis to make the double helix—each "string" of chromosomes amounting to ½ of 2π or π. Therefor in the "constant of the gravitation-interaction equation" there will be the value of π^2 (9.8696505).

In addition, since we conceive of the "synthesizing machinery" as based upon the electromagnetic radiation frequency of EPR which is equal to the difference in energy (hv) divided by h (Planck's constant) as an electron moves toward or away from a magnetic field, the net expression for the synthesizing per mass of the electron becomes:

$$\frac{(g = 2.00229) \; (u = 9.2732 \times 10^{-21} \text{ ergs/gauss}) \; (\text{H} = \text{field strength}_{gauss})}{(9.107 \times 10^{-28} \text{ gms.})}$$

If we multiply this by $\pi^2 = 9.869505$ and by the Gravitation Constant or 6.67 x 10-8, and set the product equal to the constant of Equation III or 13.59894, we can thus solve for H the field strength and we find it to be 1.0132025 well within the range we have seen in the heat-production equation Equation 7 where H varies from 1.00000 to 1.0783764. (Divide H by implicit constant 2 x 10⁹.)

110 for July 17, 1976, pg. 36 on the studies by Richard E. Dickerson of CalTech on electron transfer via cytochrome function. He believes respiration evolved from photosynthesis. Cf. Bruce S. McEwen on interactions between hormones and nerve tissues in the Scientific American for July 1976, pg. 48. The great physicist Niels Bohr suggested that thought is governed by quantum effects, etc.

Using these values we may re-state Equation III in the following manner:

$$(13.59894 \text{ ergs.}) \frac{\text{Body Weight}^{\frac{1}{2}}{}_{gms} \times \text{Body Weight}^{\frac{1}{2}}{}_{gms}}{r^2} = r \times \text{Pulse Freq}_{ergs/cm^2}$$
$$\frac{}{\text{gm}}$$

in which the gravitation force equation is interacting with kinetic energy of life-process growth.

It is at this point that we may be able to consider how it is that the bioplasma field strength (H) appears—on net balance—to be so small. It is of course not small but in reality is constantly "cooled" to the temperature range compatible with life-process. (In view of the lower temperature range of cancer cells and their inability to withstand the heat of electromagnetic radiation frequency as well as normal cells are apt to do, this matter may become of critical importance—i.e. the mitigation of the field strength H so that life-process growth may take place in the bioplasma.)

In this respect it is important to know that paramagnetic susceptibility is dependent critically upon temperature and for a number of substances is inversely proportional to the absolute temperature. This was demonstrated in 1895 by Pierre Curie and its equation is known as Curie's Law.

(A full discussion of the impact of Curie's Law and of the relation of the Bohr magneton to the Curie constant must be postponed.)*

* * * * * * * *

(7) *Brief Comment on the New Work (1976) by Nobel Laureate Albert Szent-Györgyi: "Electron Biology and Cancer—A New Theory of Cancer."*

In this brilliant little book, Szent-Györgyi, starting from the cell itself along conventional routes of biochemistry, also arrives at the basic importance of free unpaired electrons. While he notes that they give the EPR signal, he does not however take the mathematic route and the mathematic implication, in any way. Neither does he connect movement of electrons from electron donors to electron acceptors with any concept of brain-heart control through the bloodstream as a "traveling transducer," nor with general mathematic laws of growth or heat-production, as I do here. He entertains no "bioplasma concept" nor is he pursuing the phenomena of pulsing, sentience, and genderization.

---

*Cf. a succinct and clear discussion in Linus Pauling's *The Nature of the Chemical Bond*, Third Edition, 1960-1967, Cornell University Press, pg. 612.

But what he does establish, very brilliantly, based on his long and striking career, is the concept that each cell is composed of a primitive process of potentially unrestrained proliferation—the *alpha* state—and a more highly evolved tissue-specific structured protein synthesis—the *beta* state. The former proteins are colorless and may be created by fermentation. The latter—the beta state—proteins are colored due to the interaction of free electrons with photons. Cell division involves a regression—under control—to the primitive proliferating *alpha* state. Certain chemicals, e.g. dicarbonyls, act to support and stabilize structure, and thus hopefully to inhibit the wild proliferation potentiality of each cell.

While this brilliant approach is biochemical upon the established routes of biochemistry, yet it is possible that Szent-Györgyi's "Electron Biology" and that of my own bioplasma premise and my concept of life process as life process growth may one day find aspects in common.*

In the battle against cancer, all allies and all recruits to new and hopefully effective concepts, are intensely welcome.

.December 26, 1976   Daniel E. Schneider, M.D.
61 East 93rd Street
New York, N.Y. 10028

---

*For example, his division into *alpha state* and *beta state* has a certain similarity to my concept of the division of the "basic template" into a life-process maintenance portion (TDM_{lpm}) and a growth portion, species specific, in relation to brain-heart-gender growth (TDM_{bhgg})... However, the differences would lie in my concept of the many brain-oscillations now known (including the heart EKG and nerve-muscle "action currents") as growth-related to what takes place in the growth of every body cell... So too my concept postulates possible communication from the "growth-oscillations" of every cell to the prefrontal-temporal-limbic complex (the para-conscious), making possible "growth-change dreams," e.g. the forewarning cancer dreams and the impregnation dream... These are matters for further research both in the paraconscious-bioplasma concept and in Szent-Györgyi's "Electron Biology."

REFERENCES

1. Schneider, Daniel E.: *The Growth Concept of Nervous Integration*, (1949) (Monograph No. 78 in Nervous and Mental Disease Monograph Series, New York, N.Y.
2. Guillemin, Roger: (cf. Extensive Review in *Medical World News* October 27, 1972
3. Schally, Andrew: Ibid.
4. Schneider, Daniel E.: *The Psychoanalyst and the Artist,* 1950. publ. by Farrar, Strauss. New York, N.Y.
5. Schneider, Daniel E.: *The Image of the Heart*, 1956. publ. by International Universities Press, 1956.
6. Wetzel, Norman C.: *On the Motion of Growth*, Journ. *Growth*, vol. 1, pgs. 6-59
7. Gitlow, S.E.; Mendlowitz, M.; Wilk, E.K.; Wolf, R.L. and Bertani, L.M. *J. Lab. Clin. Med.*, vol. 72, no. 4, pg. 612, 1960.
8. Ketchum, A.S. (personal communication) (cf. Sindilar, W.F. and Ketchum, A.S.: Symposium on Cancer Regression, Johns Hopkins Medical School, published by C.B. Moseby, pgs. 156-172, 1975
9. Pribram, K.H. and Gill, M.M.: Freud's *Project* Re-assessed, publ. by Basic Books, New York, N.Y. 1976
10. Schneider, Daniel E. and Clarke, C.C.: *The Electroencephalo-cardiogram*. (1938) cf. Discussion in *The Image of the Heart* (as above)
11. Schneider, Daniel E.: *Revolution in the Body-Mind* (Clinical Section) *1. The Paraconscious and a New Brain-Heart Dynamic* (Read on Oct. 15, 1975 before the Society for Medical Analysts at the Carnegie Endowment Center, New York, N.Y.) (In process of publication.)
12. Crick, F.H.C. *Scientific American* (On the structure and dimensions of the DNA) *cf.* excellent offprint, 1954.
13. Watson, J.D.: Molecular Biology of the Gene, publ. by W.A. Benjamin, N.Y., N.Y.
14. Cf. Also excellent review of studies in "biomagnetics" by *Marilyn Ferguson* (1973) in her *The Brain Revolution*, publ. by Bantam Books, New York, N.Y. *especially:* Chapter I citing work of R. O. Becker, Madeleine and J.M. Barnothy, and the "magneto-encephalogram" of David Cohen.